ATLAS
OF THE WORLD
COLORING BOOK

ATLAS
OF THE WORLD
COLORING BOOK

COUNTRY IDENTIFIER GUIDE
POLITICAL AND TOPOGRAPHICAL MAPS
KEY FACTS

amber
BOOKS

Editorial and design by
Amber Books Ltd
74–77 White Lion Street
London
N1 9PF
United Kingdom
www.amberbooks.co.uk
Appstore: itunes.com/apps/amberbooksltd
Facebook: www.facebook.com/amberbooks
Twitter: @amberbooks

ISBN: 978-1-78274-525-9

Project Editor: Sarah Uttridge
Design: Mark Batley
Line map artworks © Amber Books Ltd
Colour map artworks © Lovell Johns

Maps produced by Lovell Johns

Printed in Romania

1 4 6 8 10 9 7 5 3 2

Contents

Introduction   **8**

North America   **10**
USA, Canada & Mexico Overview   12
USA Political   14
USA Topographical   16
Around the Great Lakes Topographical   18
U.S. Eastern Seaboard Topographical   19
U.S. Western Seaboard to the Rockies Topographical   20
U.S. Midwest to the Rockies Topographical   21
U.S. South Topographical   22
Mississippi River Topographical   23
Hawaii Political   24
Hawaii Topographical   25
Canada Political   26
Canada Topographical   28
Canada: Ontario to the Atlantic Topographical   30
Canada: Manitoba to the Pacific Topographical   31
Canada: The North Topographical   32
The Length of The Rockies Topographical   33
Alaska Topographical   34
Mexico Political   35
Mexico Topographical   36
Mexico North Topographical   37
Mexico Central Topographical   38
Mexico South and East Topographical   39

Central America   **40**
Central America Overview   42
Central America Topographical   44
Guatemala & Belize Topographical   46
Honduras Topographical   47
El Salvador Topographical   48
Nicaragua Topographical   49
Costa Rica Topographical   50
Panama Topographical   51

The Caribbean   **52**
Caribbean Political   54
Caribbean Topographical   55

Cuba Political   56
Cuba Topographical   57
Jamaica Topographical   58
Haiti & Dominican Republic Topographical   59
Puerto Rico Political   60
Puerto Rico Topographical   61

South America   **62**
South America Overview   64
Brazil Political   66
Brazil Topographical   67
Venezuela Political   68
Venezuela Topographical   69
Colombia Political   70
Colombia Topographical   71
Suriname & Guyana Political   72
Suriname & Guyana Topographical   73
The Amazon Topographical   74
French Guiana Topographical   75
Ecuador Political   76
Ecuador Topographical   77
Peru Political   78
Peru Topographical   79
Chile Political   80
Chile Topographical   81
Argentina & Uruguay Political   82
Argentina & Uruguay Topographical   83
Bolivia & Paraguay Political   84
Bolivia & Paraguay Topographical   85

Europe   **86**
Europe Overview   88
United Kingdom & Ireland Political   90
United Kingdom & Ireland Topographical   91
France Political   92
France Topographical   93
Belgium & The Netherlands Political   94
Belgium and The Netherlands Topographical   95
Germany Political   96
Germany Topographical   97

Norway, Sweden & Denmark Political 98
Norway, Sweden & Denmark Topographical 99
Greenland Topographical 100
Iceland Topographical 101
Finland Topographical 102
Poland Topographical 103
Belarus Topographical 104
Ukraine Topographical 105
Czech Republic & Slovakia Topographical 106
The Alps Topographical 107
Switzerland Topographical 108
Austria Topographical 109
Vatican City Topographical 110
Monaco Topographical 111
Italy Political 112
Italy Topographical 113
Spain & Portugal Political 114
Spain & Portugal Topographical 115
Balkan States Political 116
Balkan States Topographical 117
Hungary Topographical 118
Islands in the Mediterranean Topographical 119
Greece Political 120
Greece Topographical 121
Romania & Bulgaria Topographical 122
Albania Topographical 123
Macedonia Topographical 124
Serbia Topographical 125
Croatia Topographical 126
Bosnia Topographical 127

Asia **128**
Asia Overview 130
Russia Overview 132
Russia West of the Urals Topographical 134
Russia East of the Urals Topographical 135
The Caucasus Topographical 136
Armenia Topographical 137
Georgia Topographical 138
Azerbaijan Topographical 139
Central Asia Political 140
Kazakhstan Topographical 141
China Political 142
China Topographical 144

Northern China Topographical 146
West China Topographical 147
East China Topographical 148
Mongolia Topographical 149
Japan Political 150
Japan Topographical 152
North & South Korea Political 154
North & South Korea Topographical 155
Vietnam Political 156
Vietnam Topographical 157
Cambodia & Laos Topographical 158
Taiwan Topographical 159
Thailand Topographical 160
Malaysia Topographical 161
Indonesia & Papua New Guinea
   Topographical 162
The Philippines Topographical 163
Burma Topographical 164
Sri Lanka Topographical 165
India Political 166
India Topographical 167
Bangladesh Topographical 168
Pakistan Topographical 169
Nepal, Bhutan, Tibet &
   The Himalayas Topographical 170
Afghanistan Political 171
Uzbekistan, Turkmenistan, Kyrgyzstan & Tajikistan
   Topographical 172
South Pacific Islands Topographical 173

Middle East **174**
Middle East Overview 176
Turkey Political 178
Turkey Topographical 180
Syria Political 182
Syria Topographical 183
Israel, Lebanon & Jordan Political 184
Israel, Lebanon & Jordan Topographical 185
Iraq & Kuwait Topographical 186
Saudi Arabia, Yemen, Oman & Gulf States
   Topographical 187
Iran Political 188
Iran Topographical 189

Africa — 190

Africa Overview — 192
Egypt Topographical — 194
Algeria Topographical — 195
DRC Congo Topographical — 196
Tanzania Topographical — 197
Kenya Topographical — 198
Sudan Topographical — 199
Nigeria Topographical — 200
Niger Topographical — 201
Ethiopia Topographical — 202
The Nile — 203
North Africa Political — 204
North Africa Topographical — 205
West Africa Political — 206
West Africa Topographical — 207
Central Africa Political — 208
Central Africa Topographical — 209
South Africa Political — 210
South Africa Topographical — 211
Southern African Countries Political — 212
Southern African countries Topographical — 213
The Horn of Africa Topographical — 214
Madagascar Topographical — 215

Australasia — 216

Australia Political — 218
Australia Topographical — 219
New Zealand Political — 220
New Zealand Topographical — 221

Antarctica — 222

Antarctica Topographical — 224

Introduction

From the arid deserts of Africa, to the tropical rainforests of Asia and the frozen continent of Antarctica, this book features countries from every continent. Sit back, relax and choose which map you'd like to complete – perhaps an overview of USA, Canada & Mexico, a political map of Colombia, a topographical map of North & South Korea or a political map of the Southern African countries. Transport yourself to whichever country or continent you feel like...

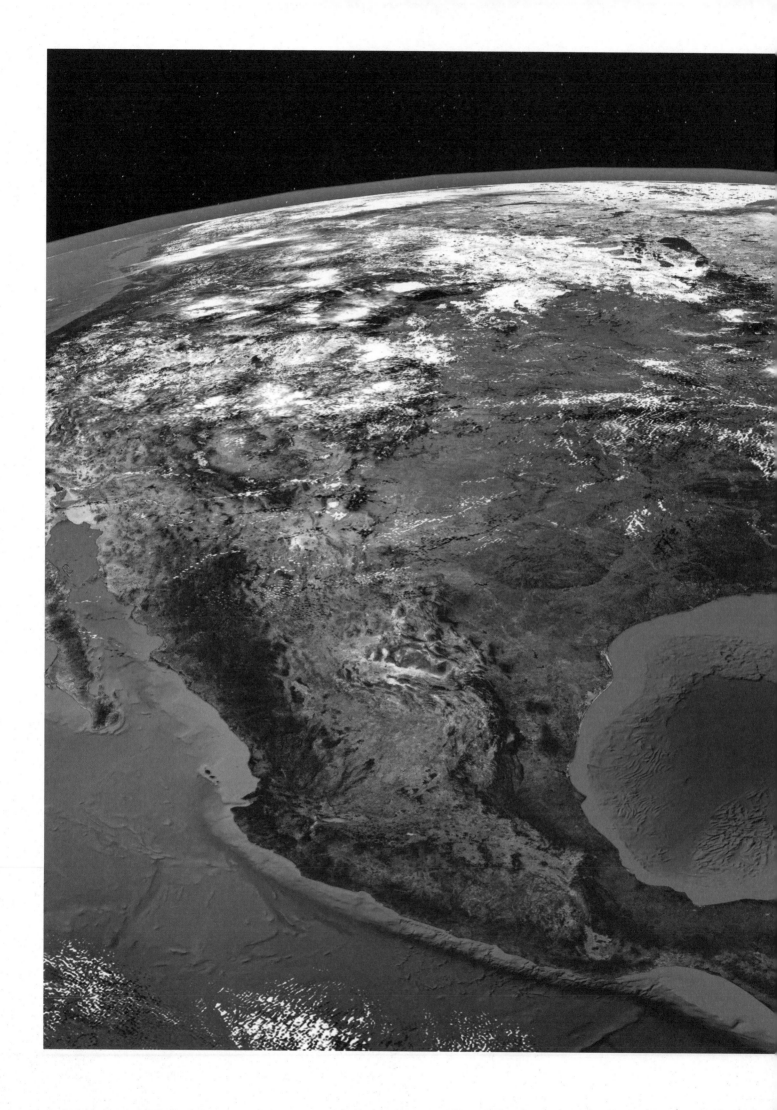

NORTH AMERICA

North America is the third-largest continent in the world, covering an area of 9,540,000 sq mi (24,709,000 sq km), or approximately 4.8% of the Earth's total surface.

USA, Canada & Mexico Overview

Canada is the largest North American country, followed by the USA and then Mexico.

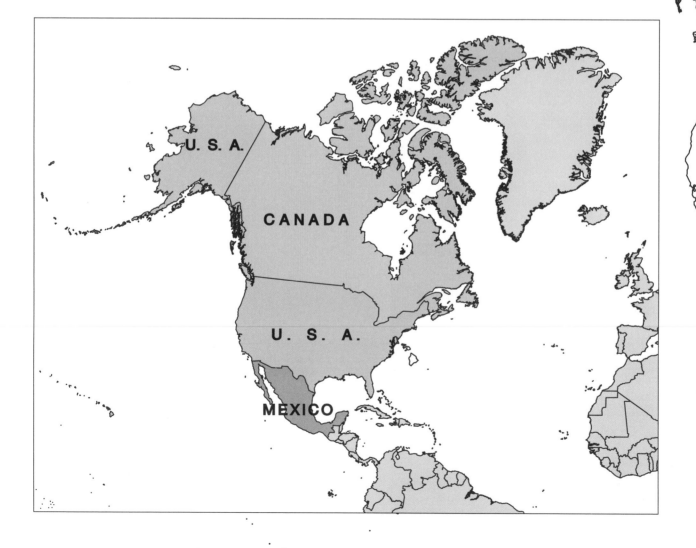

USA Political

The USA is divided into 50 states
(Hawaii and Alaska are not shown
on this map).

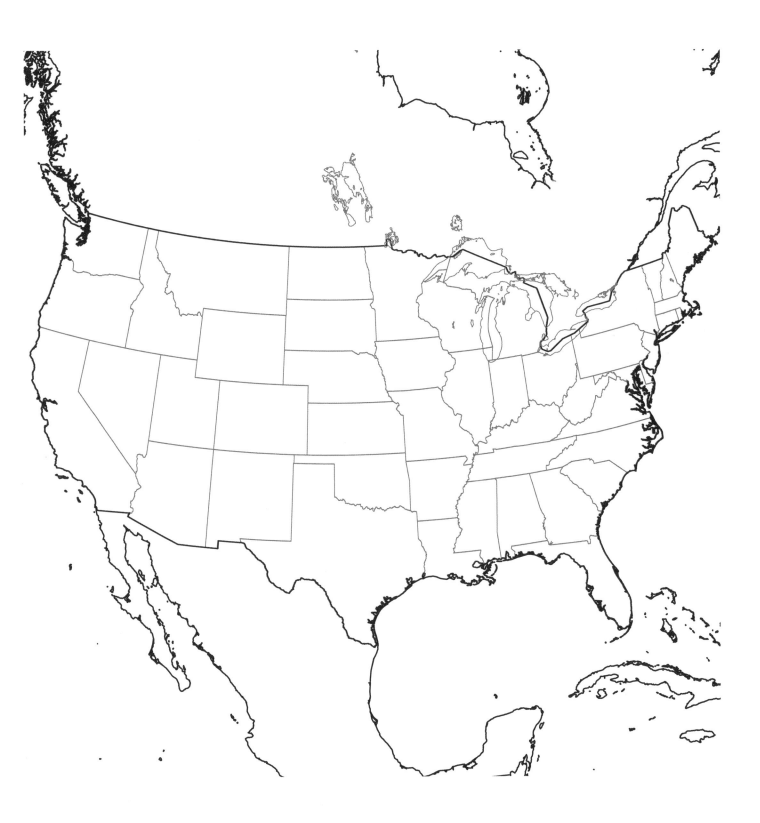

USA Topographical

The USA is the fourth-largest country in the world, covering an area of 3,796,742 sq mi (9,833,517) sq km.

Around the Great Lakes Topographical

The Great Lakes are the largest expanse of freshwater in the world. The area of all the Great Lakes is 95,160 sq mi (246,463 sq km).

U.S. Eastern Seaboard Topographical

The Eastern Seaboard extends from Maine in the north down to Florida in the south.

U.S. Western Seaboard to the Rockies Topographical

California is the most populous of the western states, with 39.2 million people living there.

U.S. Midwest to the Rockies Topographical

The U.S. Midwest extends north and west from the Ohio River to just west of the Mississippi River.

U.S. South Topographical

Florida is the most populous
of the southeastern states, with
20.6 million people living there.

Mississippi River Topographical

The Mississippi River is the
second-longest river in the USA.
It is approximately 2,320 mi
(3,730 km) long.

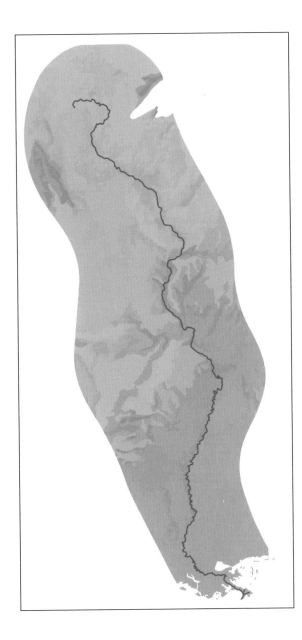

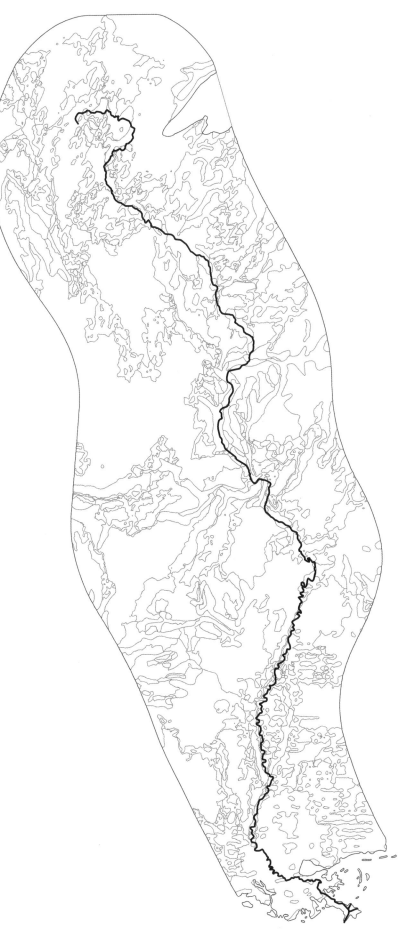

Hawaii Political

Hawaii is the only U.S. state that
is made up entirely of islands.

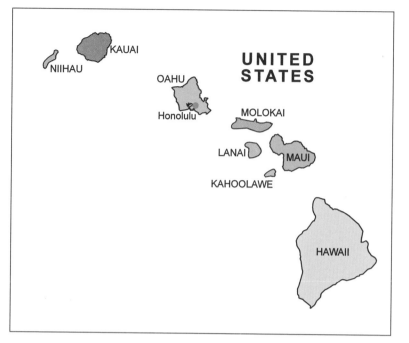

Hawaii Topographical

Hawaii consists of eight
main islands: Niihau, Kauai,
Oahu, Maui, Molokai, Lanai,
Kahoolawe and the Big Island
of Hawaii.

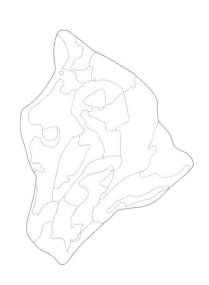

Canada Political

Canada is divided into 10 provinces. Nunavut is the largest, with an area of 808,185 sq mi (2,093,190 sq km).

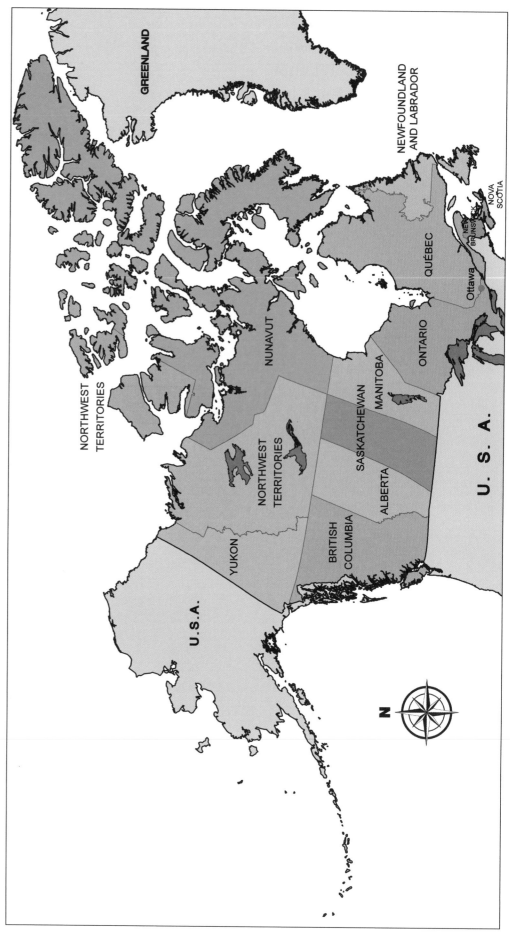

Canada Topographical

Canada is the second-largest
country in the world. It covers
3,855,103 sq mi (9,984,670 sq km).

Canada: Ontario to the Atlantic Topographical

Ontario is Canada's second-largest province and is home to one in three Canadians.

Canada: Manitoba to the Pacific Topographical

British Columbia is the westernmost province of Canada and has a population of more than four million.

Canada: The North Topographical

Yukon, Northwest Territories and
Nunavut make up the Northern
territories of Canada.

The Length of The Rockies Topographical

The Canadian Rockies span
the provinces of British
Columbia and Alberta.

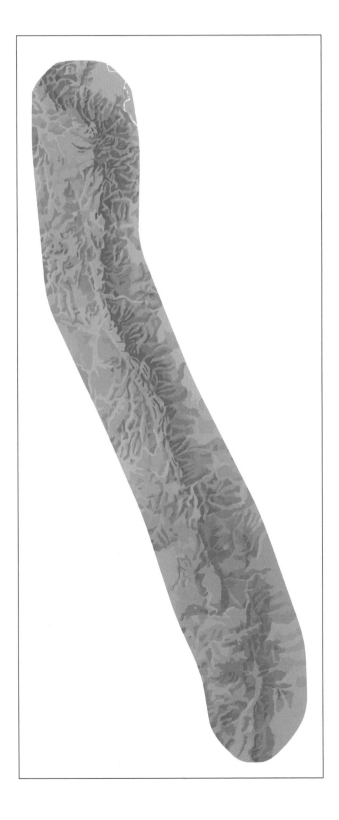

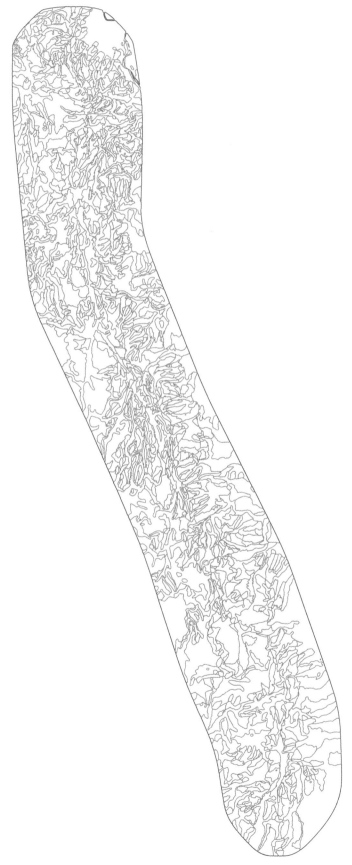

Alaska Topographical

Alaska is the largest
and most sparsely
populated U.S. state.

N

Mexico Political

Mexico is bordered to the
north by the USA and is
divided into 31 states.

Mexico Topographical

Mexico covers an area of 758,449
sq mi (1,964,375 sq km).

Mexico North Topographical

Northern Mexico is a vast
desert region bordering
the USA.

Mexico Central Topographical

Mexico City is the capital and the most populous city of Mexico. It covers an area of 573 sq mi (1,485 sq km).

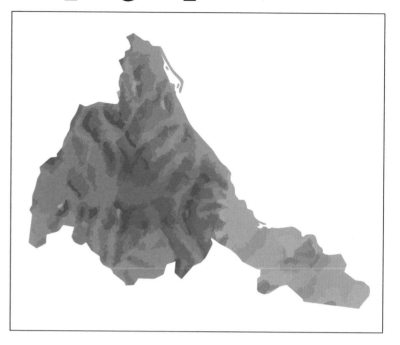

Mexico South and East Topographical

Mexico is bordered in the south by the Pacific Ocean and the countries of Belize and Guatemala.

CENTRAL AMERICA

Central America links North America with South America and covers an area of 202,265 sq mi (523,865 sq km).

Central America Overview

Central America consists
of seven countries:
Belize, Guatemala, El
Salvador, Honduras,
Nicaragua, Costa Rica
and Panama.

Central America Topographical

Central America is bordered by
Mexico to the north, Colombia to
the southeast, the Caribbean Sea to
the east, and the Pacific Ocean to
the west.

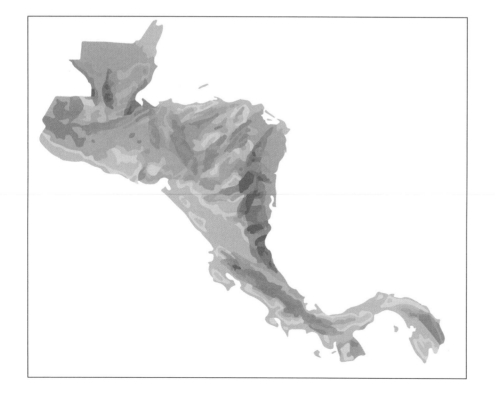

Guatemala & Belize Topographical

Guatemala and Belize have been embroiled in a territorial dispute over land and maritime boundaries since the nineteenth century.

Honduras Topographical

Honduras, in the north-central part of Central America, covers an area of 43,278 sq mi (112,090 sq km).

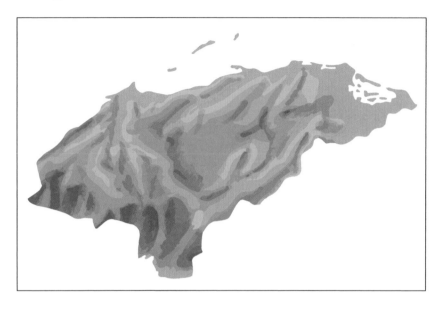

El Salvador Topographical

El Salvador is the smallest
country in Central America,
covering an area of 8,124 sq mi
(21,041 sq km).

Nicaragua Topographical

Nicaragua is the largest country in Central America, covering an area of 50,336 sq mi (130,370 sq km).

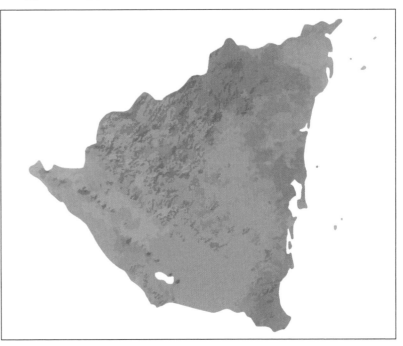

Costa Rica Topographical

Costa Rica is mainly a coastal plain
separated by rugged mountains.
It covers an area of 19,730 sq mi
(51,100 sq km).

Panama Topographical

Panama is the southernmost
of the Central American
countries, covering an area of
29,120 sq mi (75,420 sq km).

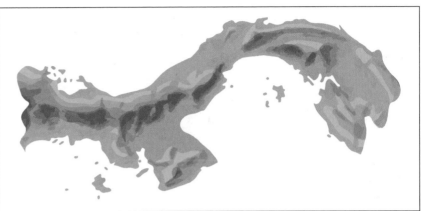

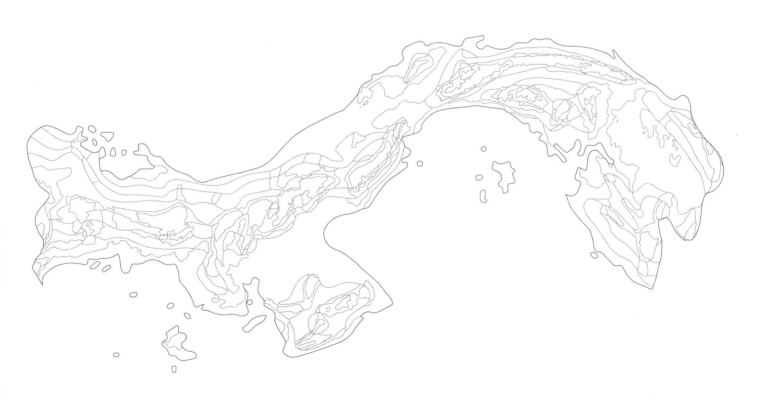

THE CARIBBEAN

The Caribbean is a group of islands in the Caribbean Sea. These islands curve southwards from the bottom tip of Florida to the northwest of Venezuela in South America.

Caribbean Political

The Caribbean is divided into 30
territories, including sovereign
states, overseas departments and
dependencies.

Caribbean Topographical

The Caribbean comprises
more than 700 islands, islets,
reefs and cays.

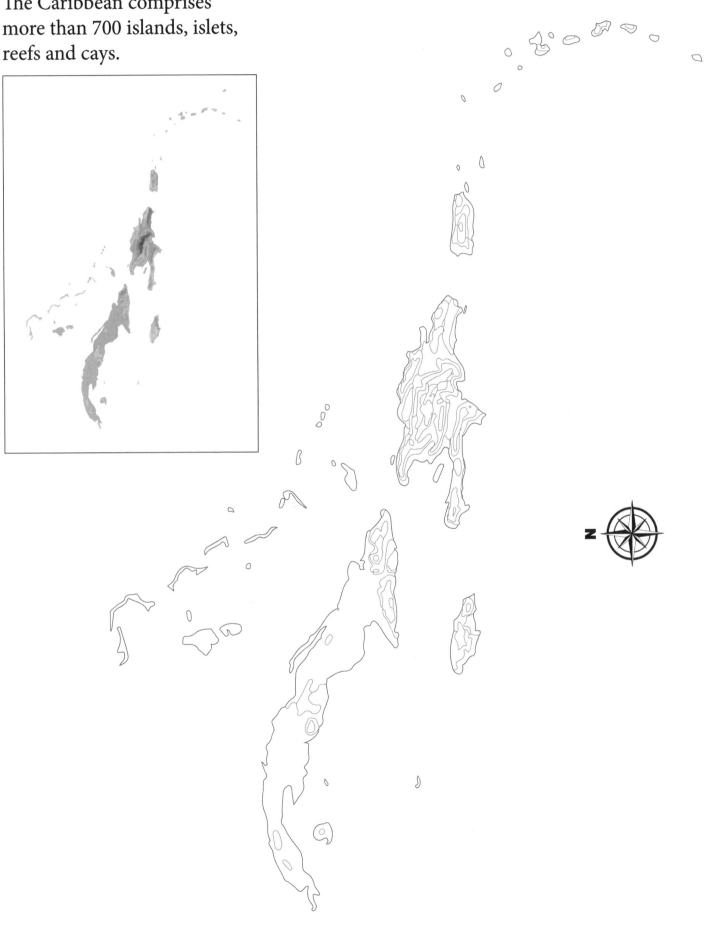

Cuba Political

Cuba is divided into 15 provinces
and one special municipality.

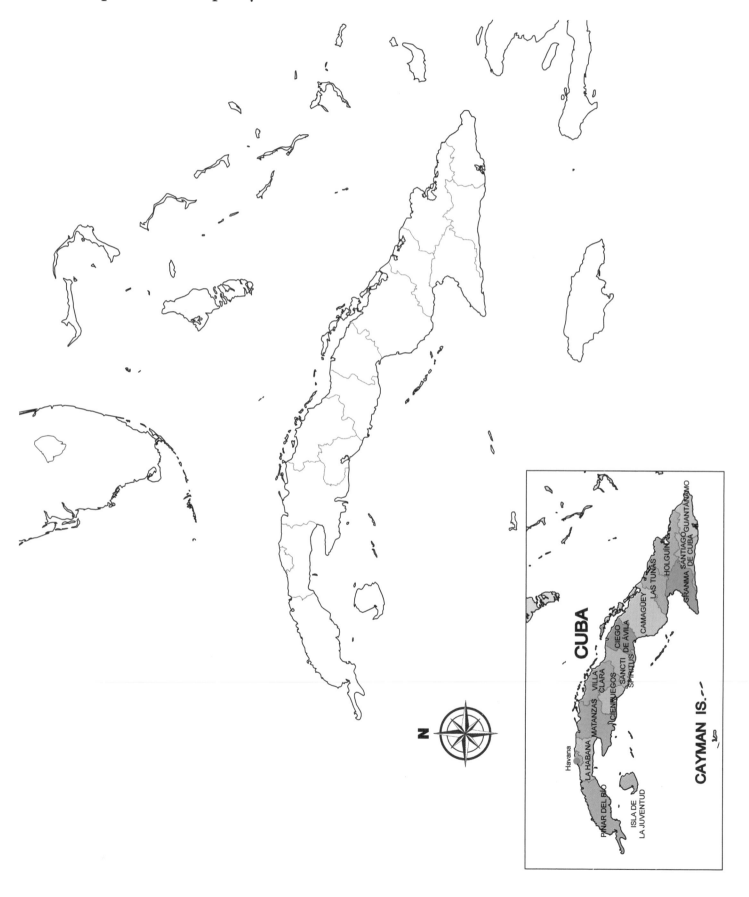

CUBA

CAYMAN IS.

Havana

PINAR DEL RÍO

ISLA DE
LA JUVENTUD

LA HABANA

MATANZAS

VILLA
CLARA

CIENFUEGOS

SANCTI
SPÍRITUS

CIEGO
DE ÁVILA

CAMAGÜEY

LAS TUNAS

HOLGUÍN

GRANMA

SANTIAGO
DE CUBA

GUANTÁNAMO

N

Cuba Topographical

Cuba is the largest Caribbean island, covering 42,803 sq mi (110,860 sq km).

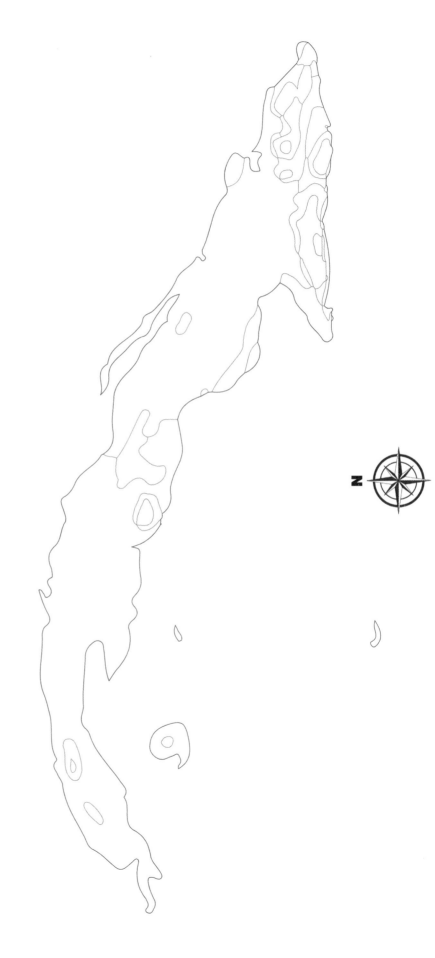

Jamaica Topographical

The fourth-largest Caribbean
island, Jamaica, covers an area of
4,244 sq mi (10,991 sq km).

Haiti & Dominican Republic Topographical

Hispaniola is home to the
Dominican Republic and
Haiti. It is the second-largest
Caribbean island.

Puerto Rico Political

Puerto Rico is divided into 78 municipalities.

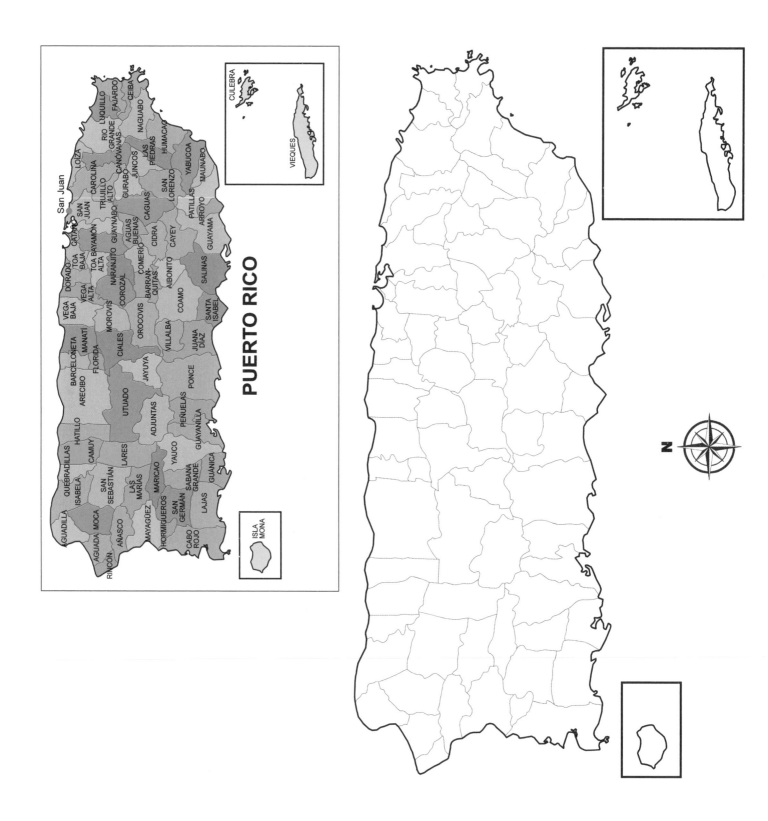

Puerto Rico Topographical

Puerto Rico covers an area of
5,325 sq mi (13,791 sq km). It
is the third-largest country in
the Caribbean.

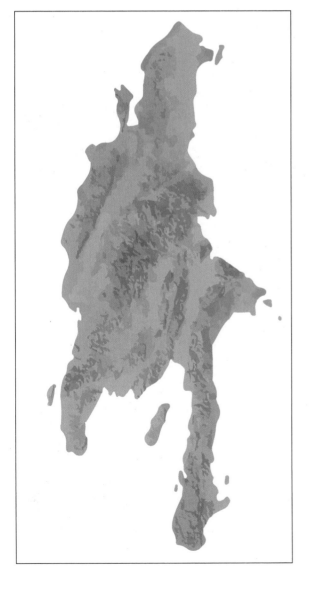

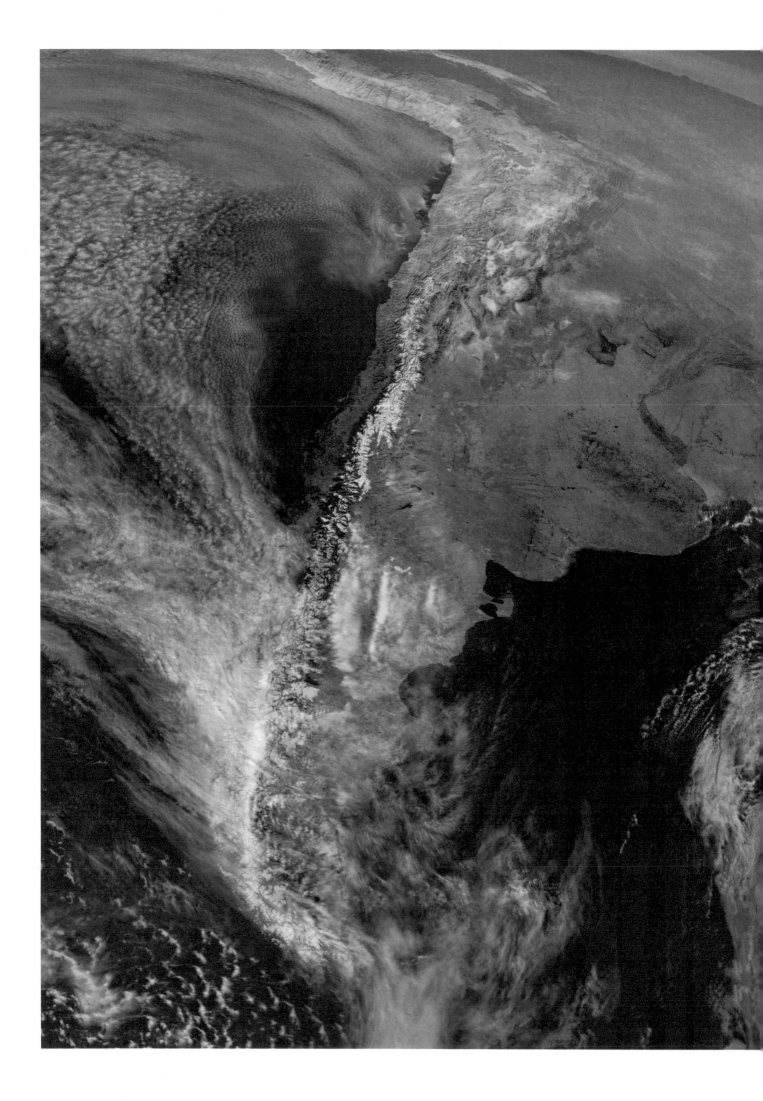

SOUTH AMERICA

South America is the fourth-largest continent in the world, covering an area of 6,890,000 sq mi (17,840,000 sq km), or approximately 12% of the Earth's total surface.

South America Overview

South America is located primarily in
the southern hemisphere. It is bordered
by the Atlantic Ocean to the east and the
Pacific Ocean to the west.

Brazil Political

Brazil is divided into 26 states and one federal state where the capital, Brasília, is located.

Brazil Topographical

Brazil is the fifth-largest country in the world, covering an area of 3,287,957 sq mi (8,515,770 sq km).

Venezuela Political

Venezuela is divided into 23
states, a capital district and the
federal dependencies, which
consist of a large number
of islands and islets on the
Caribbean Sea.

Venezuela Topographical

Venezuela covers an area of
352,144 sq mi (912,050 sq km).

Colombia Political

Colombia is at the northern tip
of South America. It is divided
into 32 departments.

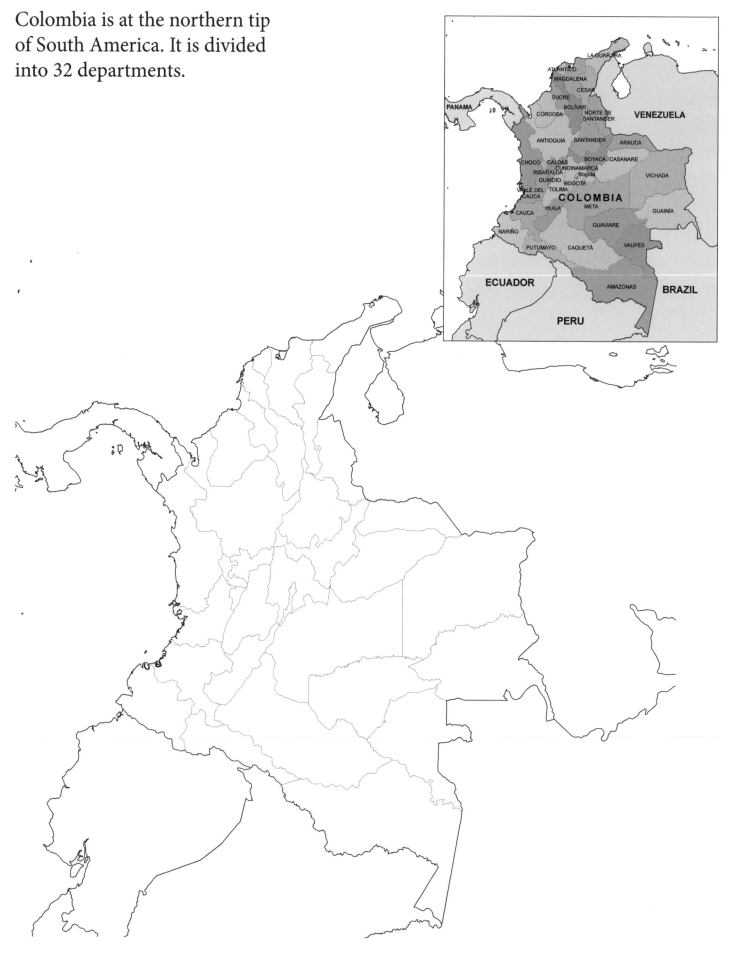

Colombia Topographical

Colombia covers an area of 439,735
sq mi (1,138,910 sq km).

Suriname & Guyana Political

Suriname and Guyana are both divided into 10 districts.

Suriname & Guyana Topographical

Suriname covers an area of
63,251 sq mi (163,820 sq km)
and Guyana covers 83,000 sq mi
(214,969 sq km).

The Amazon Topographical

The Amazon rainforest is located in Brazil, Peru and Colombia. Smaller parts are found in Venezuela, Ecuador, Bolivia, Guyana, Suriname and French Guiana.

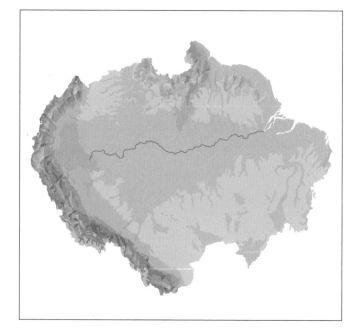

French Guiana Topographical

French Guiana is an overseas region of France on the northeast coast of South America. It covers 32,253 sq mi (83,534 sq km).

Ecuador Political

Ecuador is divided into 24
provinces. The capital, Quito,
is in Pichincha.

ECUADOR

COLOMBIA

ESMERALDAS
CARCHI
IMBABURA
SUCUMBÍOS
PICHINCHA
Quito
MANABI
NAPO
ORELLANA
COTOPAXI
LOS RIOS
TUNGURAHUA
BOLÍVAR
PASTAZA
GUAYAS
CHIMBORAZO
CAÑAR
MORONA SANTIAGO
AZUAY
EL ORO
PERU
LOJA
ZAMORA CHINCHIPE

Ecuador Topographical

Ecuador straddles the Equator
on South America's west coast.
It covers an area of 109,483 sq
mi (283,561 sq km).

Peru Political

Peru is divided into 25 regions and
the Lima Province.

ECUADOR
COLOMBIA
TUMBES
LORETO
PIURA
AMAZONAS
LAMBAYEQUE
CAJAMARCA
SAN MARTÍN
LA LIBERTAD
P E R U
BRAZIL
ANCASH
HUÁNUCO
UCAYALI
PASCO
JUNÍN
Lima
CALLAO
LIMA
MADRE DE DIOS
HUANCAVELICA
CUSCO
ICA
AYACUCHO
APURÍMAC
CALLAO
BOLIVIA
AREQUIPA
MOQUEGUA
TACNA

Peru Topographical

Peru, in western South America,
covers an area of 496,225 sq mi
(1,285,216 sq km).

Chile Political

Chile is a long, narrow country
stretching along the western edge
of South America. It is divided into
15 regions.

Chile Topographical

Chile covers an area of 291,933
sq mi (756,102 sq km).

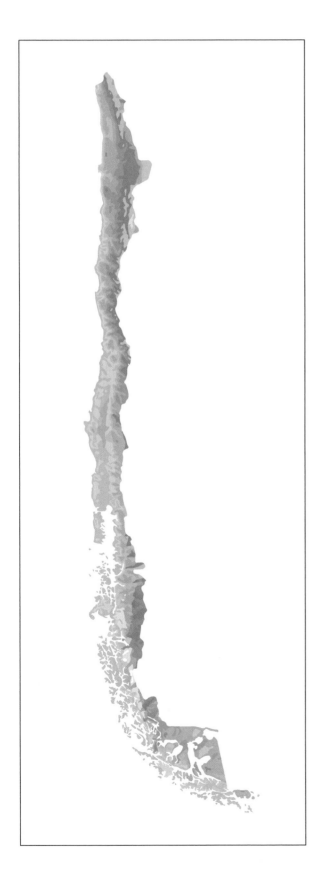

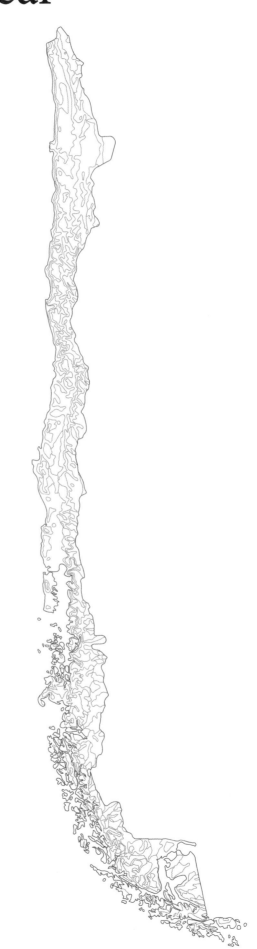

Argentina & Uruguay Political

Argentina is divided into 23
provinces and Uruguay into 19
departments.

Argentina & Uruguay Topographical

Argentina is the eighth-largest country in the world, covering 1,073,518 sq mi (2,780,400 sq km), while Uruguay covers 68,037 sq mi (176,215 sq km).

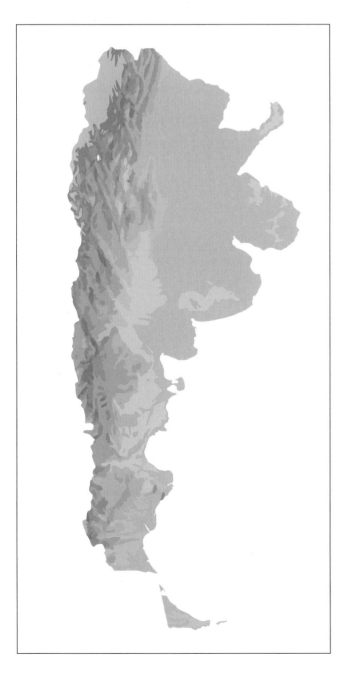

Bolivia & Paraguay Political

Bolivia is divided into nine departments and Paraguay into 17.

Bolivia & Paraguay Topographical

Bolivia covers an area of 424,164 sq mi (1,098,581 sq km), while Paraguay covers 157,047 sq mi (406,752 sq km).

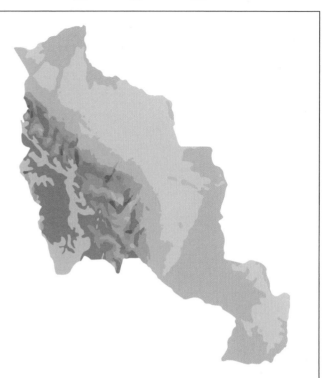

EUROPE

Europe is the second-smallest continent in the world, covering an area of 3,930,519 sq mi (10,180,000 sq km), or approximately 2% of the Earth's total surface.

Europe Overview

Europe is bordered by the Arctic
Ocean to the north, the Atlantic
Ocean to the west, and the
Mediterranean Sea to the south.
The Ural Mountains in Russia
mark the eastern extreme.

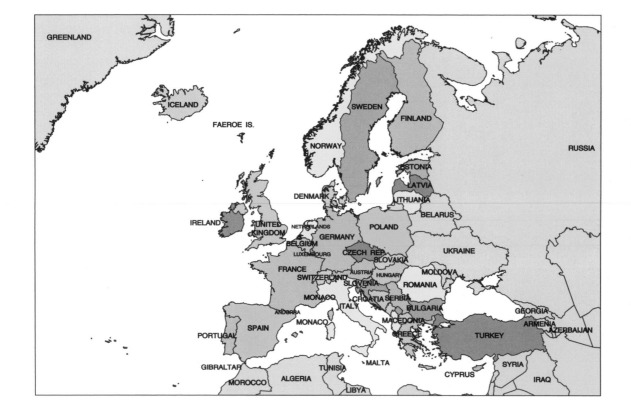

GREENLAND

ICELAND

FAEROE IS.

NORWAY

SWEDEN

FINLAND

RUSSIA

ESTONIA

LATVIA

LITHUANIA

DENMARK

BELARUS

IRELAND

UNITED
KINGDOM

NETHERLANDS

POLAND

BELGIUM

GERMANY

LUXEMBOURG

CZECH REP.

SLOVAKIA

UKRAINE

FRANCE

SWITZERLAND

AUSTRIA

HUNGARY

MOLDOVA

SLOVENIA

ROMANIA

MONACO

CROATIA SERBIA

ITALY

BULGARIA

GEORGIA

ANDORRA

MONACO

MACEDONIA

ARMENIA

AZERBAIJAN

SPAIN

GREECE

TURKEY

PORTUGAL

GIBRALTAR

TUNISIA

MALTA

SYRIA

MOROCCO

ALGERIA

CYPRUS

IRAQ

LIBYA

United Kingdom & Ireland Political

The countries within the United Kingdom and Ireland are divided into counties.

United Kingdom & Ireland Topographical

The United Kingdom and
Ireland covers an area of 121,658
sq mi (315,093 sq km) and has
a combined population of just
under 70 million.

France Political

France is divided into 13
administrative regions and five
overseas regions.

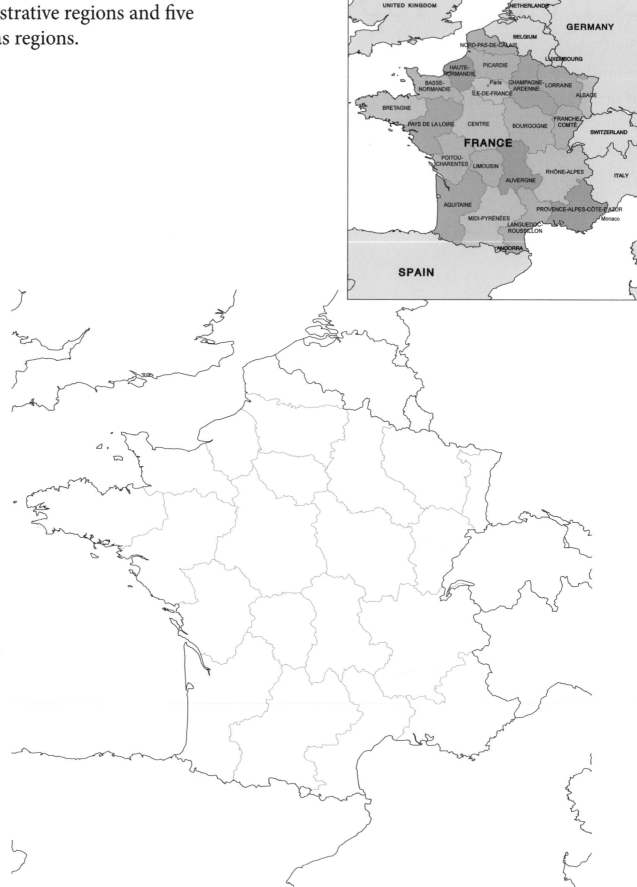

France Topographical

France, in Western Europe, covers an area of 248,573 sq mi (643,801 sq km).

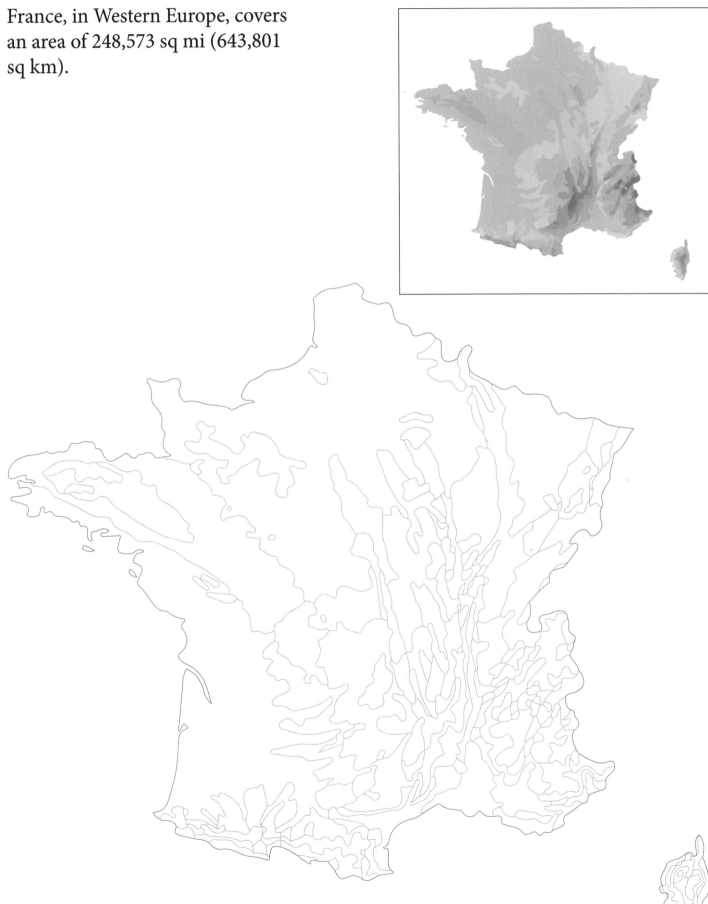

Belgium &
The Netherlands Political

Brussels is the largest city in
Belgium, while Amsterdam is
the largest in The Netherlands.

NETHERLANDS

GRONINGEN

FRIESLAND

NOORD-HOLLAND

DRENTHE

Amsterdam

FLEVOLAND

OVERIJSSEL

UTRECHT

GELDERLAND

ZUID-HOLLAND

NOORD-BRABANT

ZEELAND

LIMBURG

ANTWERP

WEST
FLANDERS

EAST
FLANDERS

LIMBURG

FLEMISH
BRABANT

Brussels

WALLOON
BRABANT

LIÈGE

HAINAUT

NAMUR

BELGIUM

LUXEMBOURG

LUXEMBOURG

FRANCE

Belgium &
The Netherlands Topographical

The area of Belgium is 11,969
sq mi (30,528 sq km), while
the Netherlands is 16,039 sq
mi (41,543 sq km).

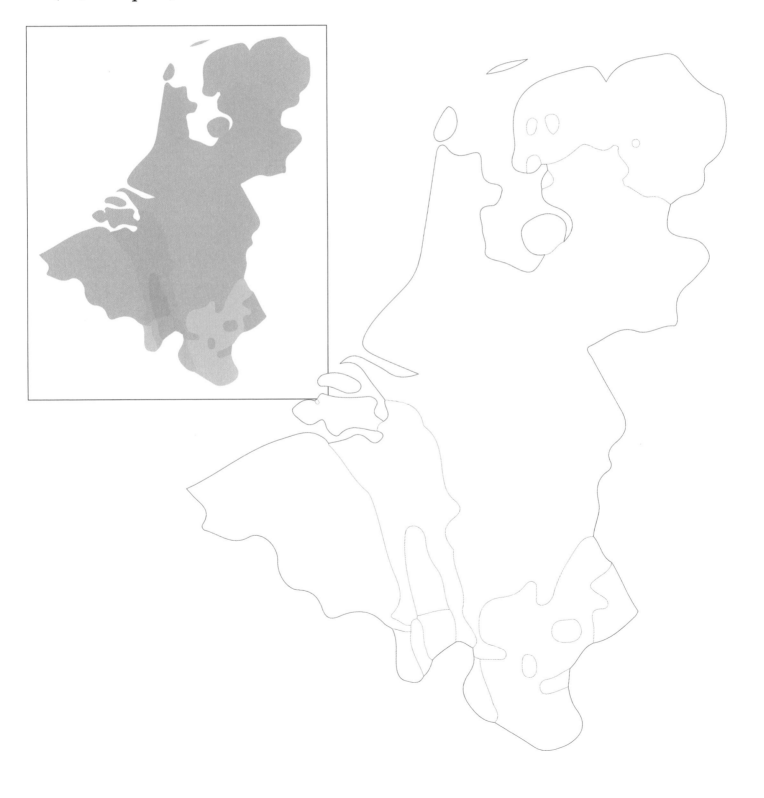

Germany Political

Germany lies in the middle of
Europe and shares borders with
nine countries. It is divided into
16 states.

Germany Topographical

Germany is the seventh-largest
country in Europe, covering an
area of 137,847 sq mi (357,021
sq km).

Norway, Sweden & Denmark Political

Sweden is the largest of the Scandinavian countries, covering an area of 173,860 sq mi, (450,295 sq km).

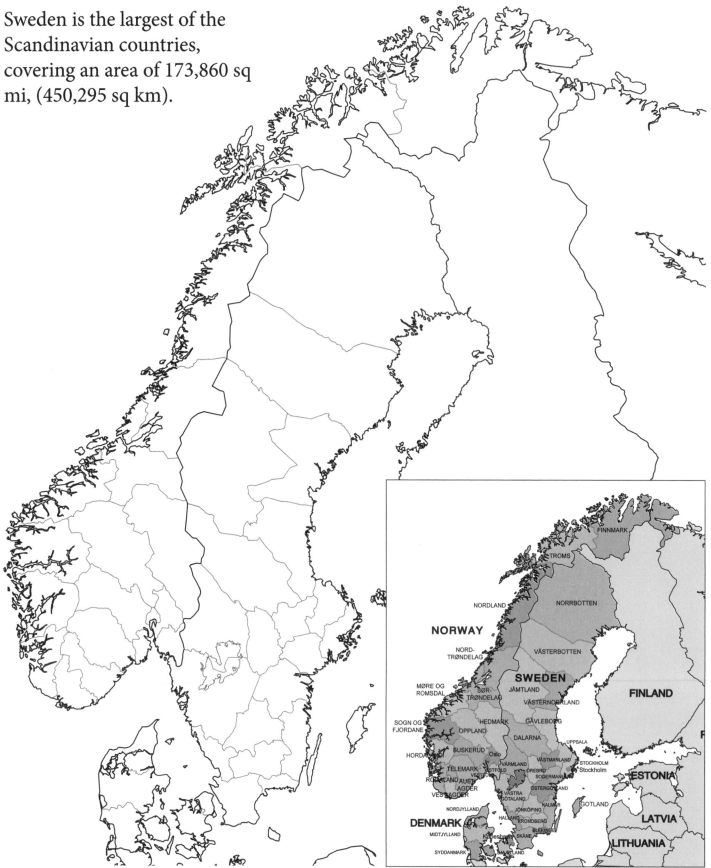

Norway, Sweden & Denmark Topographical

Norway covers an area of
125,181 sq mi (323,802 sq km)
and Denmark 16,639 sq mi
(43,094 sq km).

Greenland Topographical

Greenland is the largest island in
the world, with an area of 836,330
sq mi (2,166,086 sq km).

Iceland Topographical

Iceland is covered by ice, glaciers and geysers and covers an area of 39,768 sq mi (103,000 sq km).

Finland Topographical

Finland is the eighth-largest
country in Europe, covering
an area of 130,559 sq mi
(338,145 sq km).

Poland Topographical

Poland is the ninth-largest
country in Europe, covering
an area of 120,728 sq mi
(312,685 sq km).

Belarus Topographical

Belarus, in Eastern Europe,
covers an area of 80,155 sq mi
(207,600 sq km).

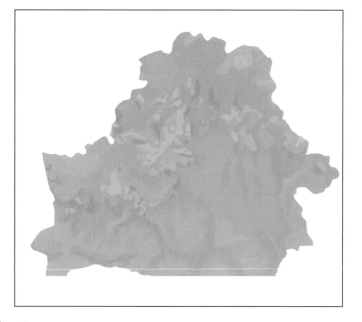

Ukraine Topographical

Ukraine is the second-largest
country in Europe after Russia.
It covers an area of 233,032 sq
mi (603,550 sq km).

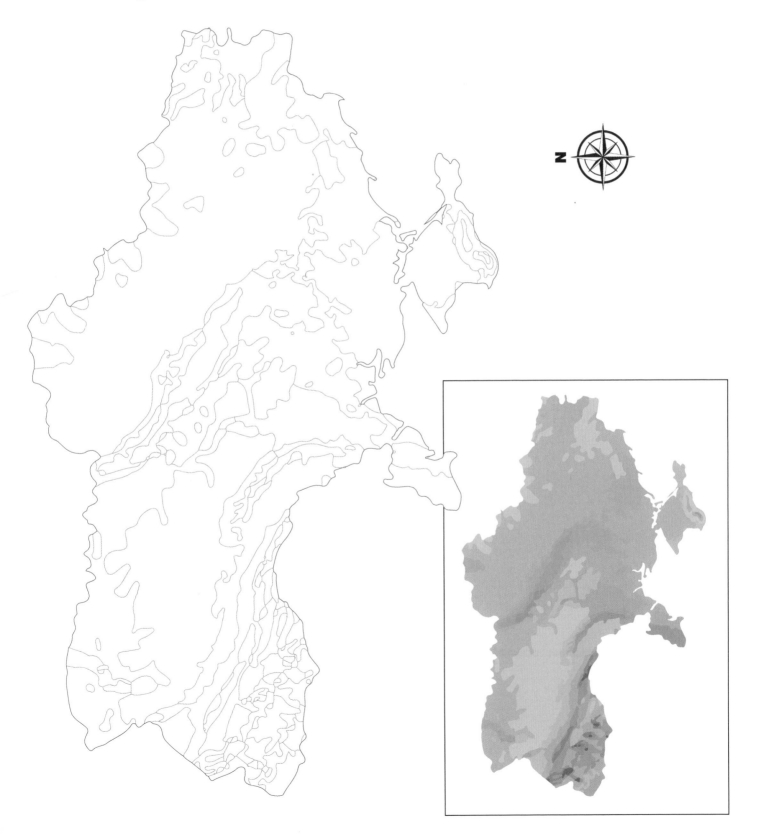

Czech Republic & Slovakia Topographical

The Czech Republic, at 30,451 sq mi (78,867 sq km), is larger than Slovakia, which covers 18,933 sq mi (49,035 sq km).

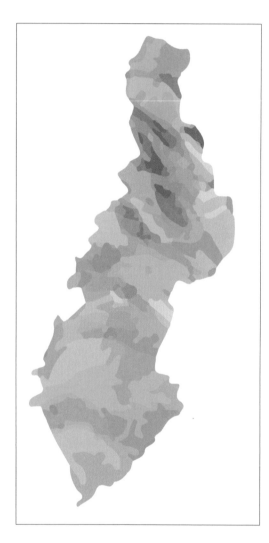

The Alps Topographical

The Alps are the highest and most extensive mountain range in Europe. They stretch about 750 mi (1,200 km) across eight countries.

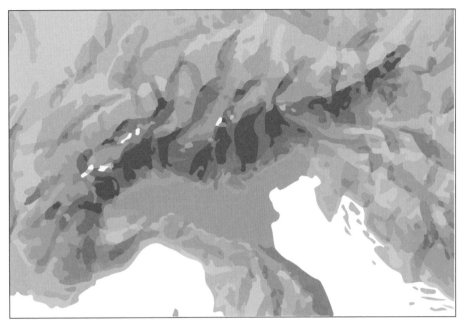

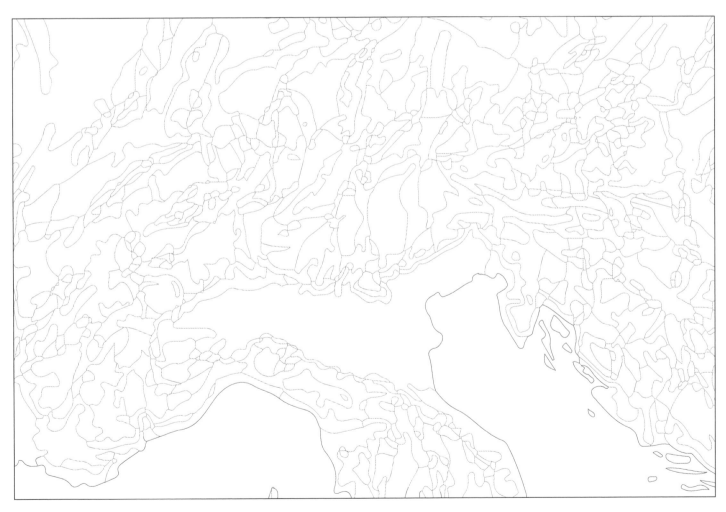

Switzerland Topographical

Switzerland, home to numerous
lakes, villages and the high peaks of
the Alps, covers an area of 15,937
sq mi (41,277 sq km).

Austria Topographical

Austria is a mountainous
country that covers an area of
32,383 sq mi (83,871 sq km).

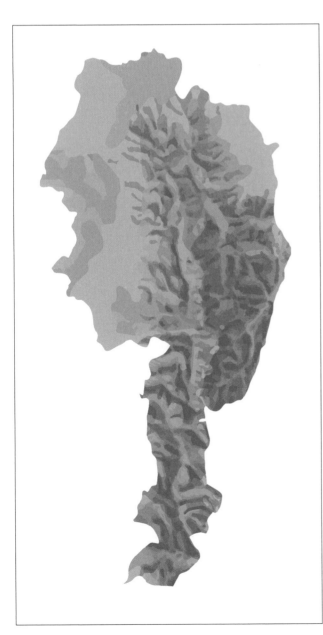

Vatican City Topographical

Vatican City is the smallest country in the world, with an area of 0.17 sq mi (0.44 sq km) and a population of around 1,000.

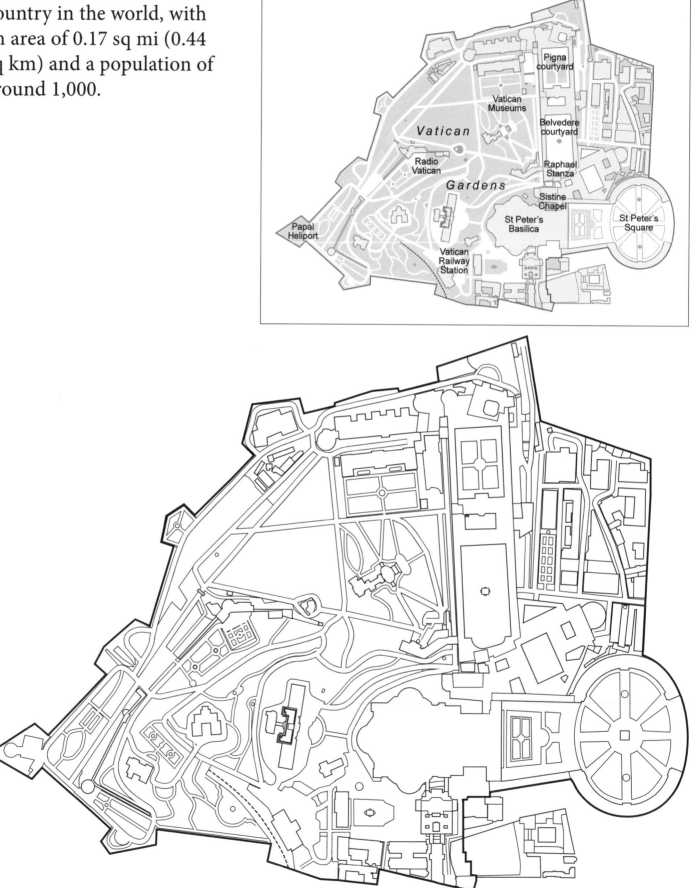

Monaco Topographical

Monaco is the second-smallest
country in the world, with an
area of 0.77 sq mi (2 sq km) and a
population of around 30,000.

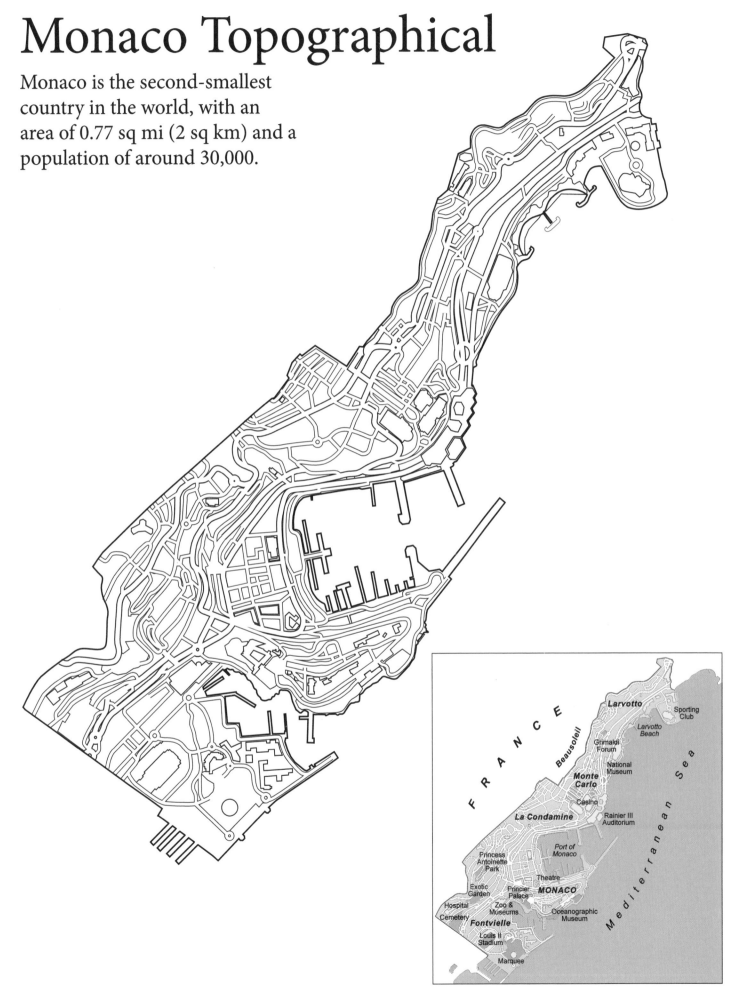

Italy Political

Italy is divided into 20 regions, and has an area of 116,348 sq mi (301,340 sq km).

Italy Topographical

Italy is the boot-shaped peninsula
that juts out of Southern Europe. It
has a long Mediterranean coastline.

Spain & Portugal Political

Spain covers an area of
195,124 sq mi (505,370 sq
km). It is the fourth-largest
country in Europe.

Spain & Portugal Topographical

Portugal is the westernmost
country of the European mainland,
covering an area of 35,556 sq mi
(92,090 sq km).

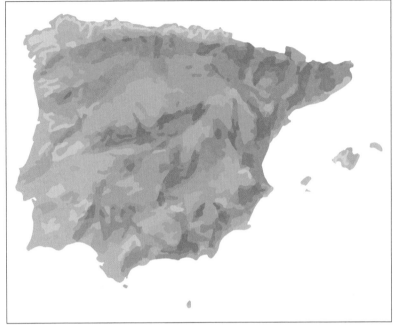

Balkan States Political

The Balkans comprise a peninsula
and a cultural area in Eastern and
Southeastern Europe with various
and disputed borders.

Balkan States Topographical

Romania is the biggest country in the Balkans, covering an area of 92,043 sq mi (238,391 sq km).

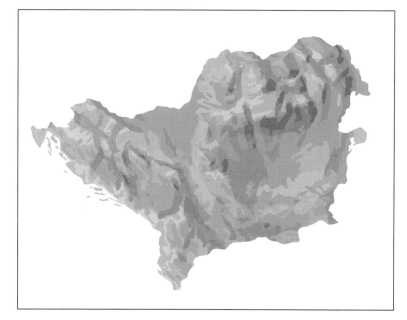

Hungary Topographical

Hungary shares a border with
seven countries and covers an area
of 35,918 sq mi (93,028 sq km).

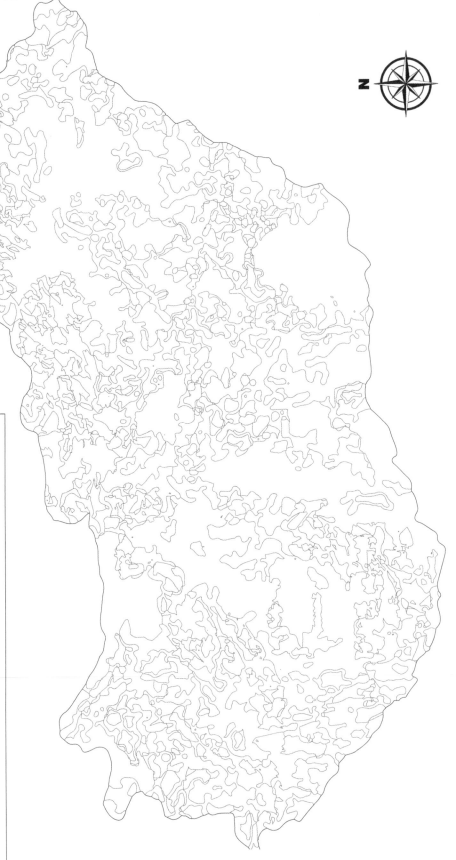

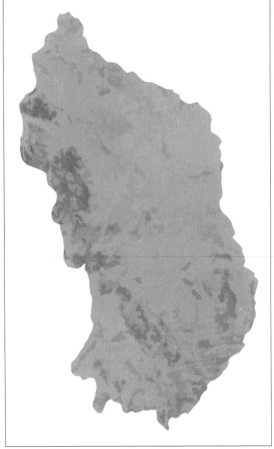

Islands in the Mediterranean Topographical

Sicily is the biggest island in the Mediterranean, followed by Sardinia and Cyprus.

Greece Political

Greece is at the crossroads of Europe, Asia and Africa. It is divided into regions and then municipalities.

Greece Topographical

About four-fifths of Greece is
mountainous, including most of
the islands.

Romania & Bulgaria Topographical

Romania covers an area of 92,043 sq mi (238,391 sq km) and Bulgaria covers 42,811 sq mi (110,879 sq km).

Albania Topographical

About 70 per cent of Albania is mountainous and rugged, and often inaccessible. It covers an area of 11,099 sq mi (28,748 sq km).

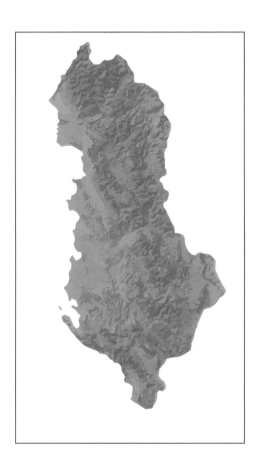

Macedonia Topographical

The landlocked country of Macedonia covers an area of 9,928 sq mi (25,713 sq km).

Serbia Topographical

Serbia, in the west-central
Balkans, covers an area of
29,913 sq mi (77,474 sq km).

Croatia Topographical

Croatia, to the east side of the
Adriatic Sea, to the east of Italy,
covers an area of 21,851 sq mi
(56,594 sq km).

Bosnia Topographical

Bosnia, next to the Adriatic
Sea, to the south of Croatia and
west of Serbia, covers an area of
19,767 sq mi (51,197 sq km).

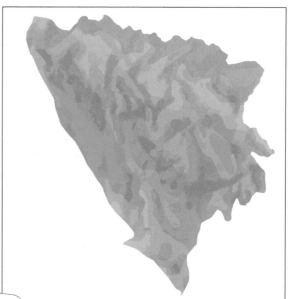

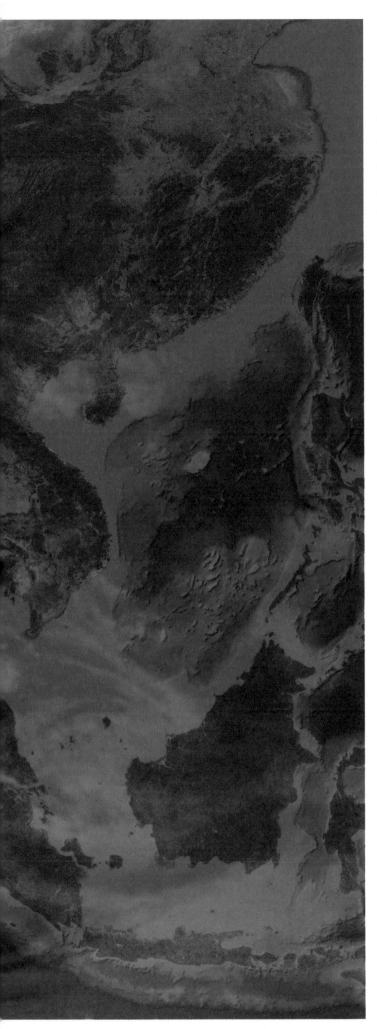

ASIA

Asia is the largest and most populous continent in the world, covering an area of 17,212,000 sq mi (44,579,000 sq km), or approximately 8.8% of the Earth's total surface.

Asia Overview

The world's largest and most
populous continent ranges from
the tropical south to the subarctic
north, and from mountains to
jungle to deserts.

Russia Overview

The world's largest country, Russia covers an area of 6,601,668 sq mi (17,098,242 sq km). It reaches from Europe across North Asia to the Pacific Ocean.

RUSSIA

FINLAND

NORWAY

SWEDEN

ESTONIA

DENMARK

LATVIA

LITHUANIA

UNITED
KINGDOM

GERMANY

POLAND

BELARUS

NETHERLANDS

CZECH
REP.

UKRAINE

KAZAKHSTAN

MONGOLIA

FRANCE

BELGIUM

AUSTRIA

HUNGARY

CROATIA

ROMANIA

MOLDOVA

MONACO

SERBIA

BULGARIA

GEORGIA

ARMENIA

UZBEKISTAN

KYRGYZSTAN

SPAIN

ITALY

BOSNIA

AZERBAIJAN

TURKMENISTAN

TAJIKISTAN

CHINA

NORTH
KOREA

JAPAN

SOUTH
KOREA

TUNISIA

MALTA

GREECE

TURKEY

CYPRUS

SYRIA

IRAQ

IRAN

AFGHANISTAN

Russia West of the Urals Topographical

The European part of Russia west of the Ural Mountains – which run north to south through the country – may account for only a fifth of the country's landmass but is home to 77% of its population.

Russia East of the Urals Topographical

One of the most sparsely populated parts of the world, Russia east of the Urals – the geographical region referred to as Siberia – is largely made up of coniferous forests. The area reaches into the Arctic Circle in the north, with the population greater in the south.

The Caucasus Topographical

Situated between the Black Sea
and the Caspian Sea, the Caucasus
links Europe to the west with Asia
to the east.

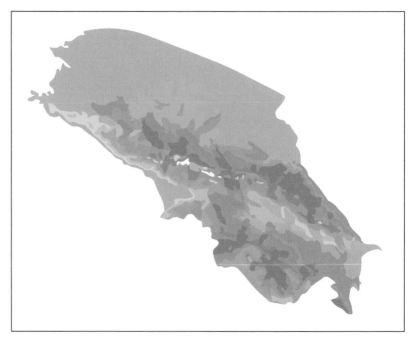

Armenia Topographical

Armenia, in the southern
Caucasus, covers an area of
11,484 sq mi (29,743 sq km).

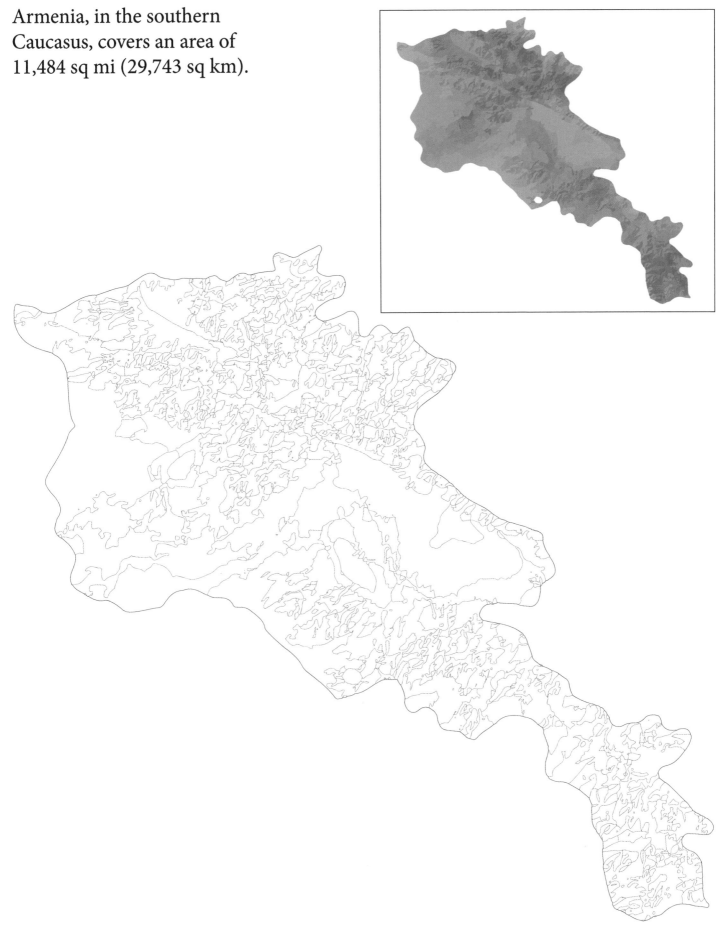

Georgia Topographical

Georgia is a largely mountainous country opening out to the Black Sea to the west. It covers an area of 26,911 sq mi (69,700 sq km).

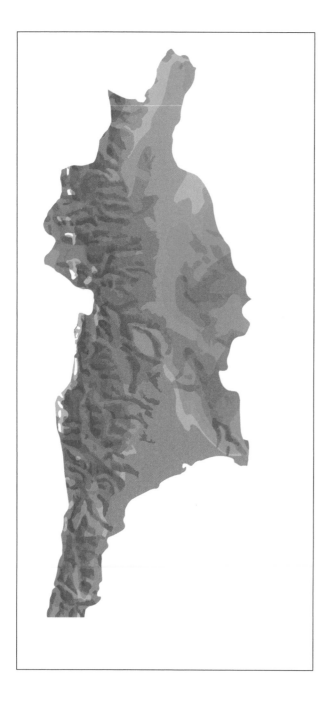

Azerbaijan Topographical

Azerbaijan covers an area of
33,437 sq mi (86,600 sq km).
More than half the country is
mountainous.

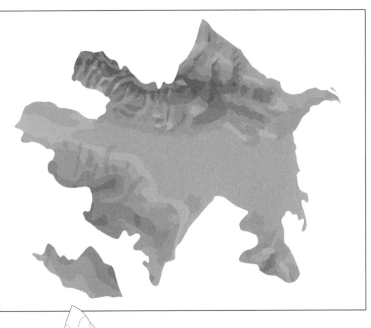

Central Asia Political

Reaching from the Caspian Sea
in the west to China in the east,
Central Asia encompasses five
countries: Kazakhstan, Uzbekistan,
Tajikistan, Turkmenistan and
Kyrgyzstan.

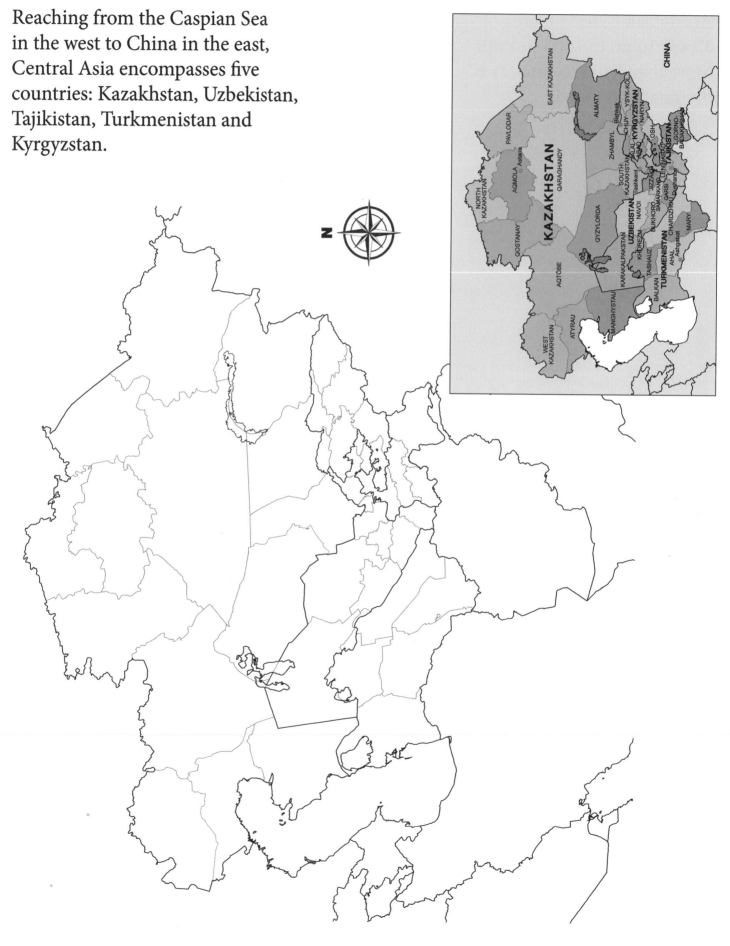

Kazakhstan Topographical

Kazakhstan is the world's ninth-largest country and the largest landlocked country. It covers an area of 1,052,090 sq mi (2,724,900 sq km).

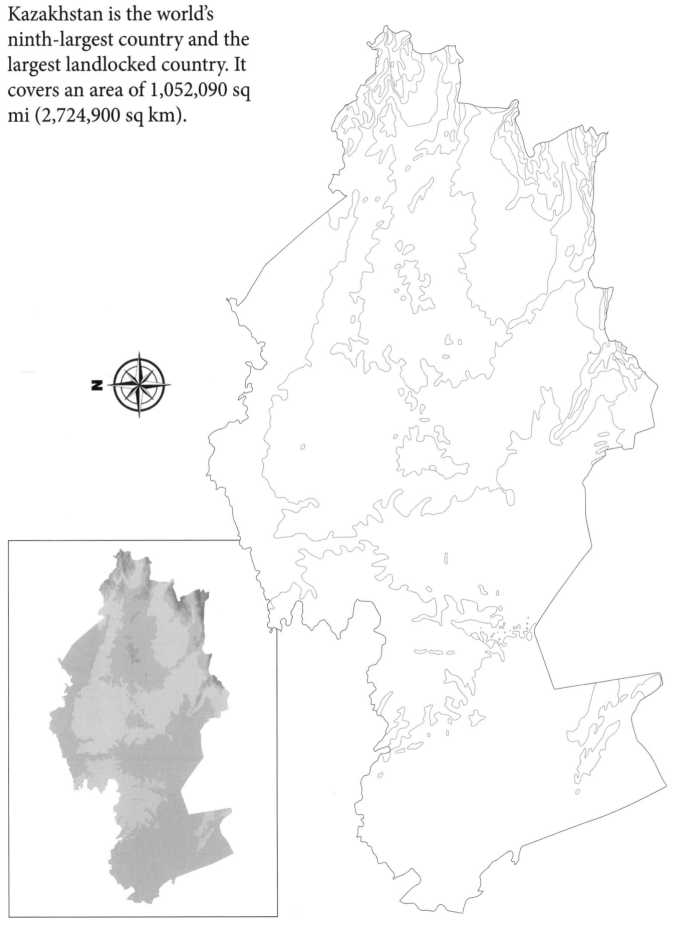

China Political

With 1.374 billion inhabitants, China is the world's most populous country. It is divided into 22 provinces, five autonomous regions and four municipalities.

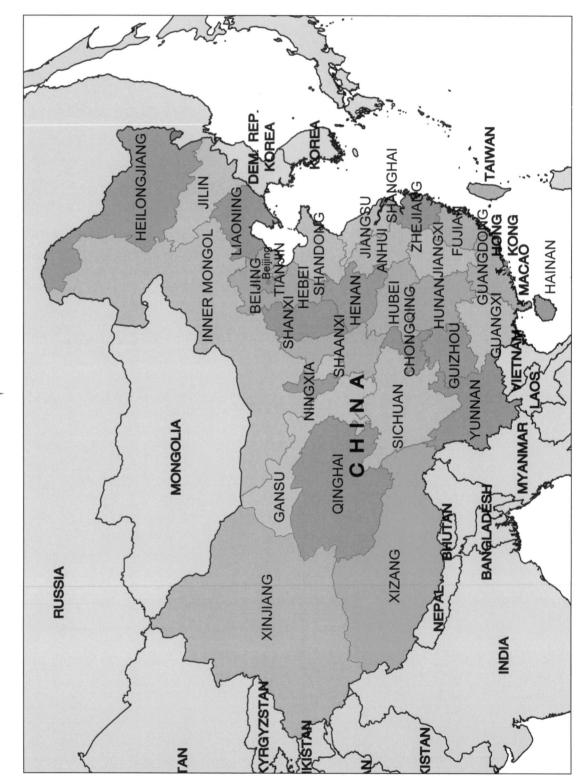

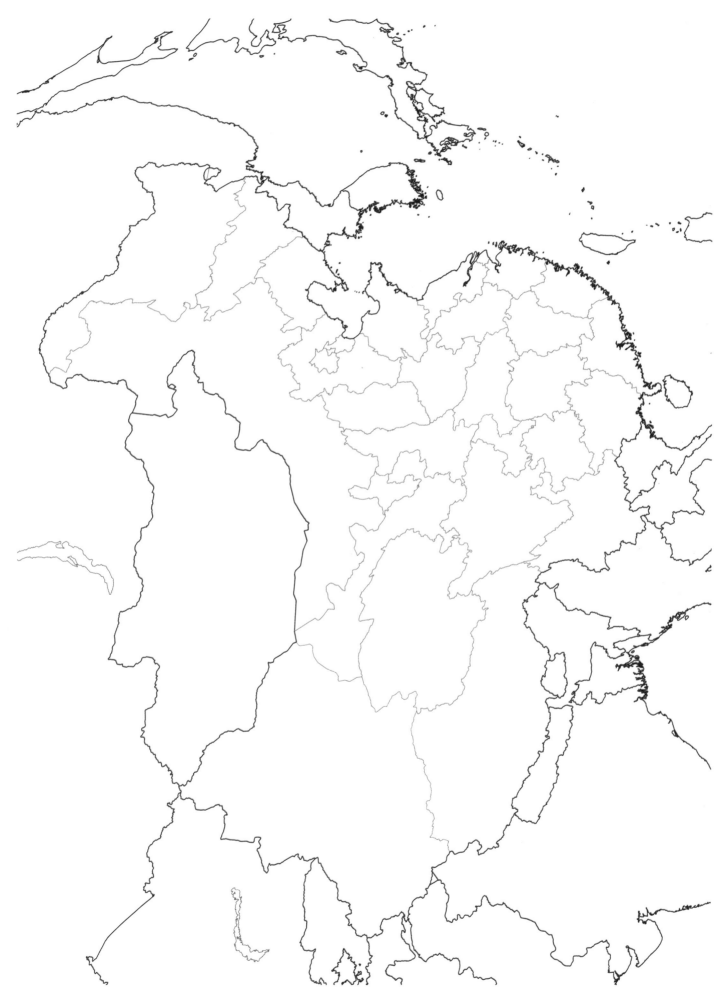

China Topographical

Covering 3,705,407 sq
mi (9,596,960 sq km),
China's terrain ranges from
mountainous to desert.

Northern China Topographical

The most northerly part of China is characterized by a largely continental climate, with the extremeties being subarctic.

West China Topographical

West China is a mix of cold
desert and tundra. In the far
south it includes the Tibet
Autonomous Region.

East China Topographical

East China is made up of plains, deltas and hills. It is the most populous part of the country.

Mongolia Topographical

Mongolia covers an area of
603,909 sq mi (1,564,116 sq
km) and is bordered by Russia
and China.

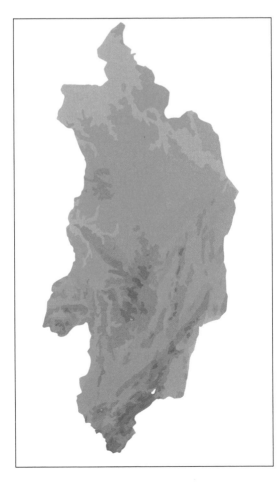

Japan Political

Japan is composed of four Home Islands
and almost 7,000 smaller islands. It is
divided into 47 prefectures.

RUSSIA

HOKKAIDO

NORTH
KOREA

SOUTH
KOREA

JAPAN

AOMORI

AKITA

IWATE

YAMAGATA   MIYAGI

NIIGATA

ISHIKAWA   FUKUSHIMA

TOYAMA   TOCHIGI

GUNMA

FUKUI   NAGANO 2.   IBARAKI

1. 3. Tokyo

HYOGO   GIFU   4. CHIBA

TOTTORI   SHIGA

SHIMANE   KYOTO   AICHI

OKAYAMA   5. MIE   SHIZUOKA

HIROSHIMA   6.   NARA

YAMAGUCHI   7.   WAKAYAMA

FUKUOKA   KOCHI

SAGA OITA   EHIME

NAGASAKI KUMAMOTO

MIYAZAKI

KAGOSHIMA

OKINAWA

1. YAMANASHI
2. SAITAMA
3. TOKYO
4. KANAGAWA
5. OSAKA
6. KAGAWA
7. TOKUSHIMA

Japan Topographical

With a landmass of 145,914 sq mi
(377,915 sq km), Japan's islands are
largely rugged and mountainous.

North & South Korea Political

The Korean Peninsula in East Asia has been divided into the countries of North and South Korea since the end of World War II. Prior to this it was recognized simply as Korea.

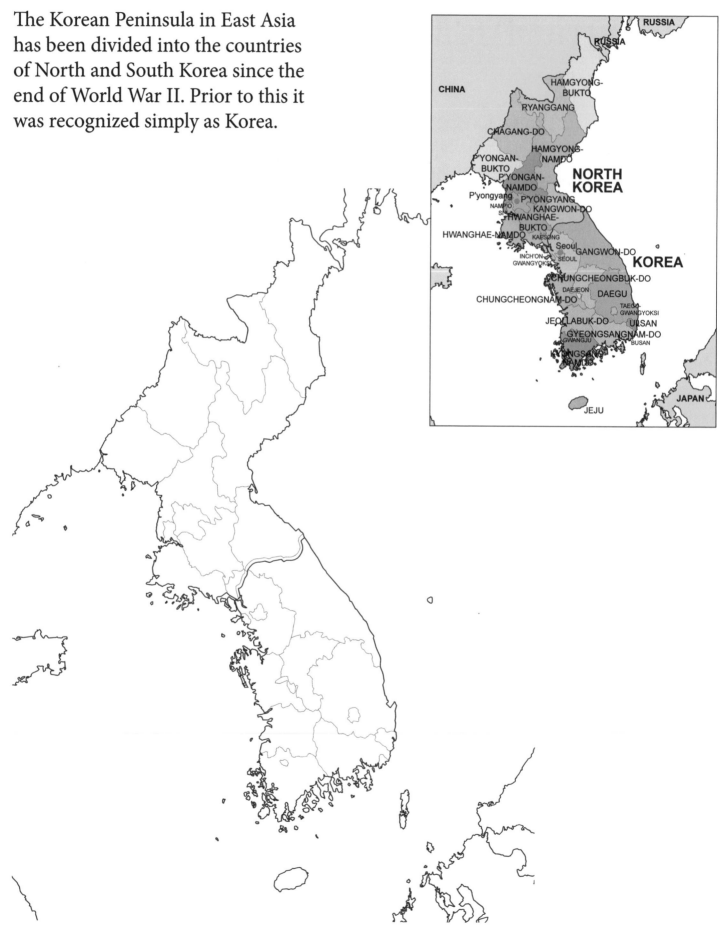

North & South Korea Topographical

About 70 per cent of the Korean Peninsula is covered by mountains. The Peninsula extends southwards from the Asian continent for approximately 683 mi (1,100 km).

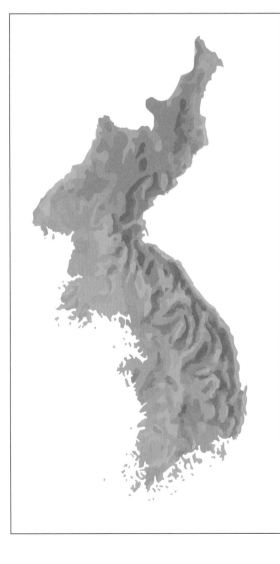

Vietnam Political

Vietnam is divided into
58 provinces and five
municipalities.

CHINA

HÀ GIANG | CAO
BẰNG
ĐIỆN | LÀO | TUYÊN | BẮC KẠN
BIÊN | CAI | QUANG | LẠNG SƠN
YÊN BÁI | THÁI NGUYÊN
PHÚ THỌ | BẮC GIANG
SƠN LA | VĨNH PHÚC | 3 | 2
HOÀ BÌNH | HÀ NỘI | HẢI
HÀ NAM | THÁI BÌNH
NINH BÌNH | NAM ĐỊNH
THANH HÓA

LAOS

1 HƯNG YÊN
2 BẮC NINH
3 HÀ NỘI
4 HẢI DƯƠNG
5 HẢI PHÒNG

NGHỆ AN

HÀ TĨNH

QUẢNG
BÌNH

QUẢNG TRỊ

THỪA THIÊN-HUẾ | ĐÀ NẴNG | **VIETNAM**

QUẢNG
THAILAND | NAM

QUẢNG NGÃI

KON
TUM | BÌNH ĐỊNH

GIA LAI

PHÚ YÊN

CAMBODIA | DAK
LAK | KHÁNH HÒA

LÂM ĐỒNG | NINH THUẬN
BÌNH PHƯỚC
TÂY NINH | BÌNH THUẬN
BÌNH DƯƠNG ĐỒNG
HỒ CHÍ MINH CITY | NAM BỘ
ĐỒNG THÁP | LONG AN | BÀ RỊA-VŨNG TÀU
AN GIANG
CẦN THƠ
HẬU GIANG | BẾN TRE
KIÊN GIANG | TRÀ VINH
SÓC TRĂNG
BẠC LIÊU
CÀ MAU

Vietnam Topographical

Vietnam covers 127,881
sq mi (331,210 sq km).
Its climate ranges from
monsoonal in the north to
tropical in the south.

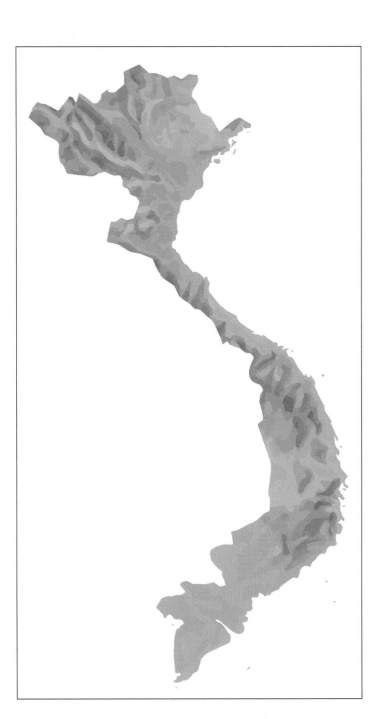

Cambodia & Laos Topographical

Cambodia covers an area of
69,898 sq mi (181,035 sq km)
and Laos an area of 91,428 sq
mi (236,800 sq km).

Taiwan Topographical

The tropical island of Taiwan
covers an area of 13,892 sq mi
(35,980 sq km).

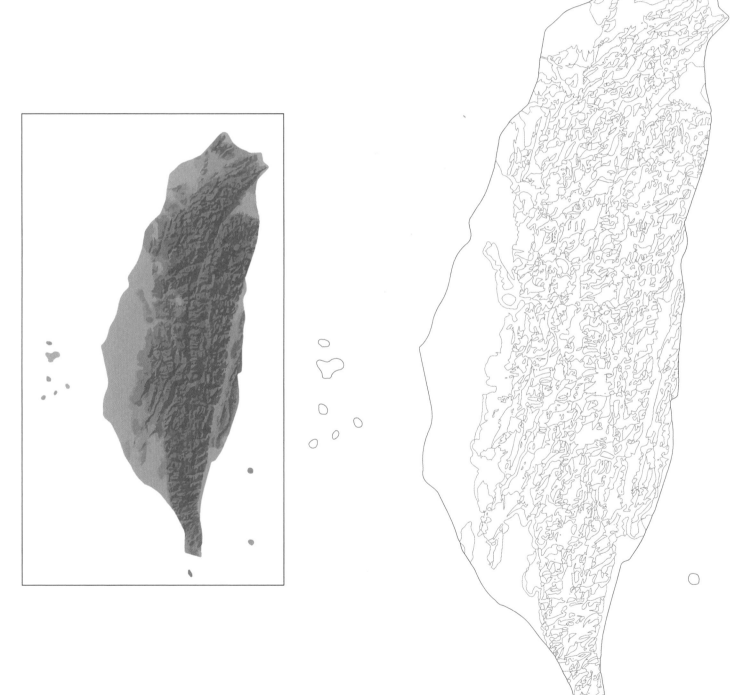

Thailand Topographical

Thailand covers 198,117 sq
mi (513,120 sq km) and has a
population of 68 million.

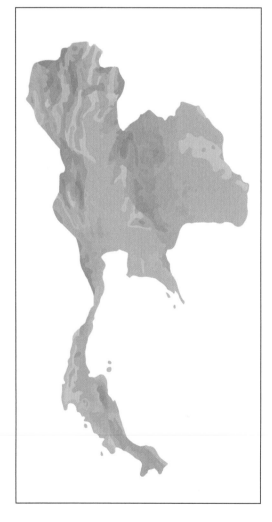

Malaysia Topographical

Spanning one-third of the
island of Borneo and the
peninsula bordering southern
Thailand, Malaysia covers
127,355 sq mi (329,847 sq km).

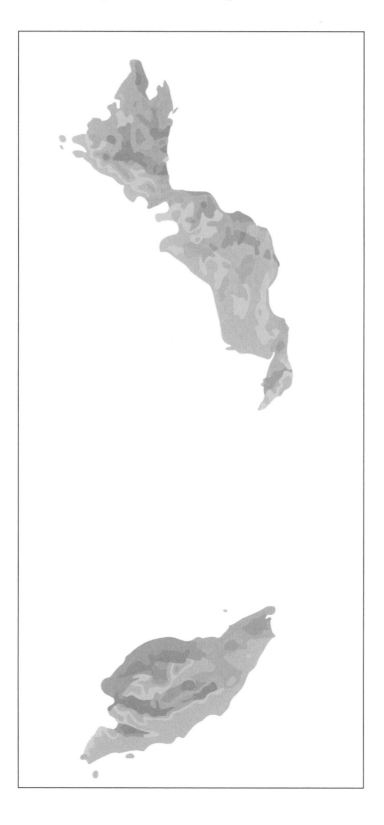

Indonesia & Papua New Guinea Topographical

The archipelago of Indonesia covers 735,358 sq mi (1,904,569 sq km). Papua New Guinea, the eastern half of the island of New Guinea, and its islands cover 178,703 sq mi (462,840 sq km).

The Philippines Topographical

Covering 115,831 sq mi
(300,000 sq km), the
Philippines is a largely
mountainous country.

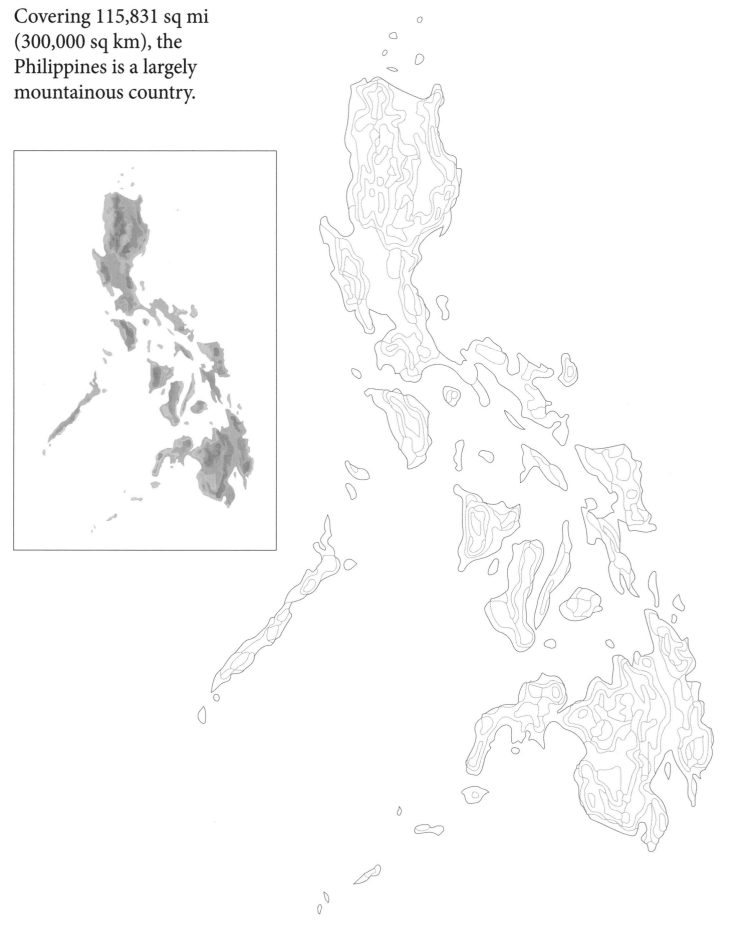

Burma Topographical

A country of tropical lowlands ringed
by rugged highlands, Burma covers
261,228 sq mi (676,578 sq km).

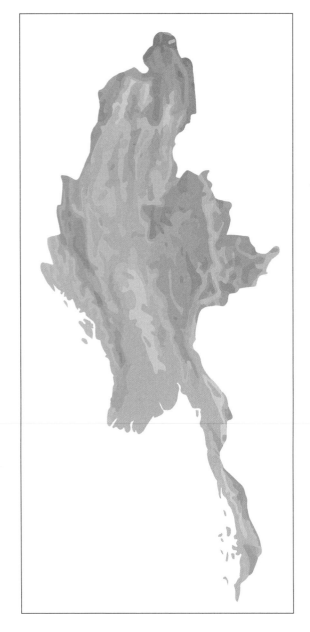

Sri Lanka Topographical

The island of Sri Lanka covers
25,332 sq mi (65,610 sq km).

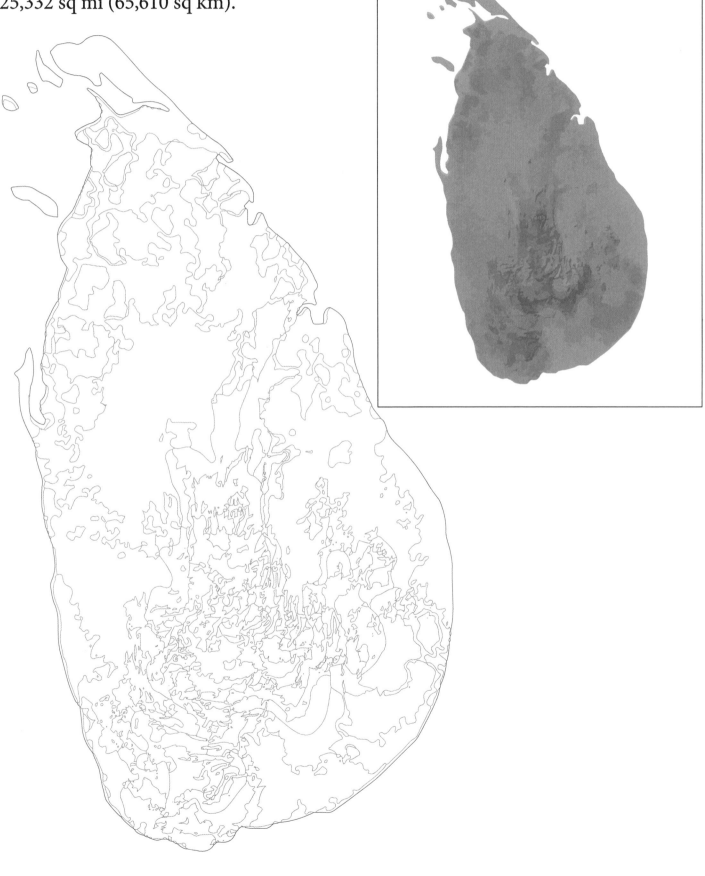

India Political

India has a population of 1.26 billion. It is divided into 29 states and seven union territories.

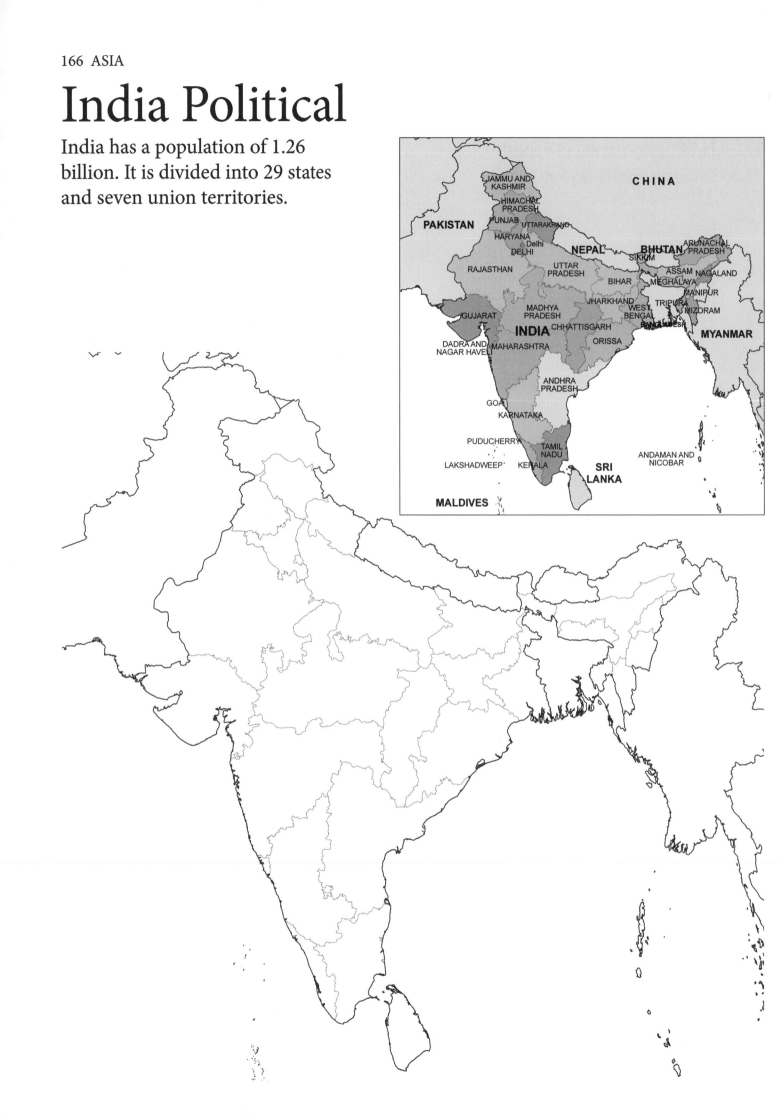

India Topographical

India is the seventh-largest country
in the world, covering an area of
1,269,219 sq mi (3,287,263 sq km).

Bangladesh Topographical

The almost entirely flat country
of Bangladesh covers an area of
57,321 sq mi (148,460 sq km).

Pakistan Topographical

Pakistan is the sixth-most
populous country in the world
and covers an area of 307,374
sq mi (796,095 sq km).

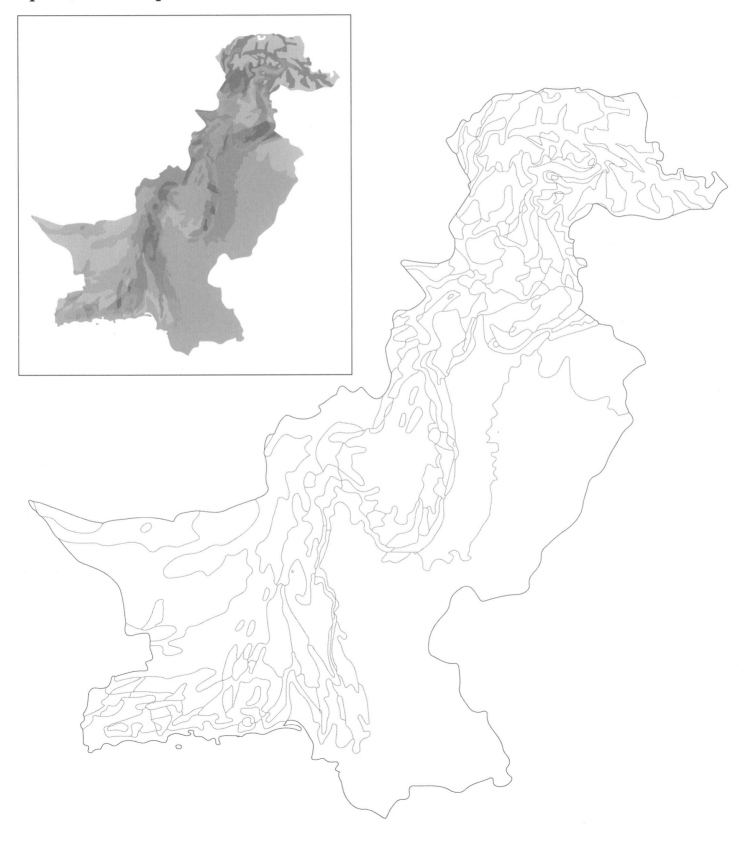

Nepal, Bhutan, Tibet & The Himalayas Topographical

The Himalayan mountain range spreads across five countries: Bhutan, India, Nepal, China and Pakistan. It includes more than 100 mountains.

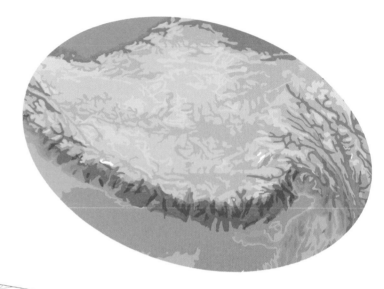

Afghanistan Topographical

The landlocked country of
Afghanistan covers an area of
251,827 sq mi (652,230 sq km).

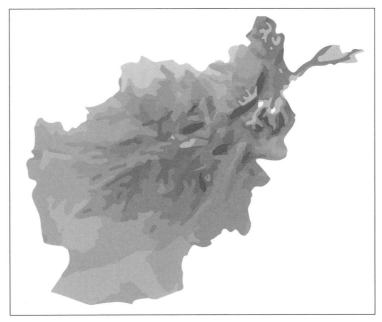

Uzbekistan, Turkmenistan, Kyrgyzstan & Tajikistan Topographical

Tucked between India, Russia and China, the 'stans' are a congregation of mountains, steppe grassland and desert.

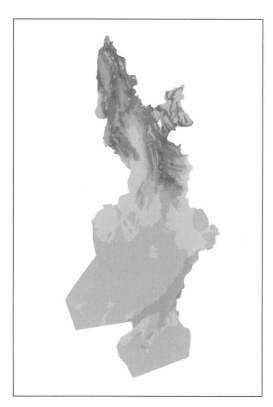

South Pacific Islands Topographical

The South Pacific islands are divided into the Polynesian islands, which include Samoa, Tonga, Cook Islands, French Polynesia and Easter Island, while Fiji, New Caledonia, Vanuatu and the Solomon Islands are the Melanesian islands.

SAMOA

FIJI

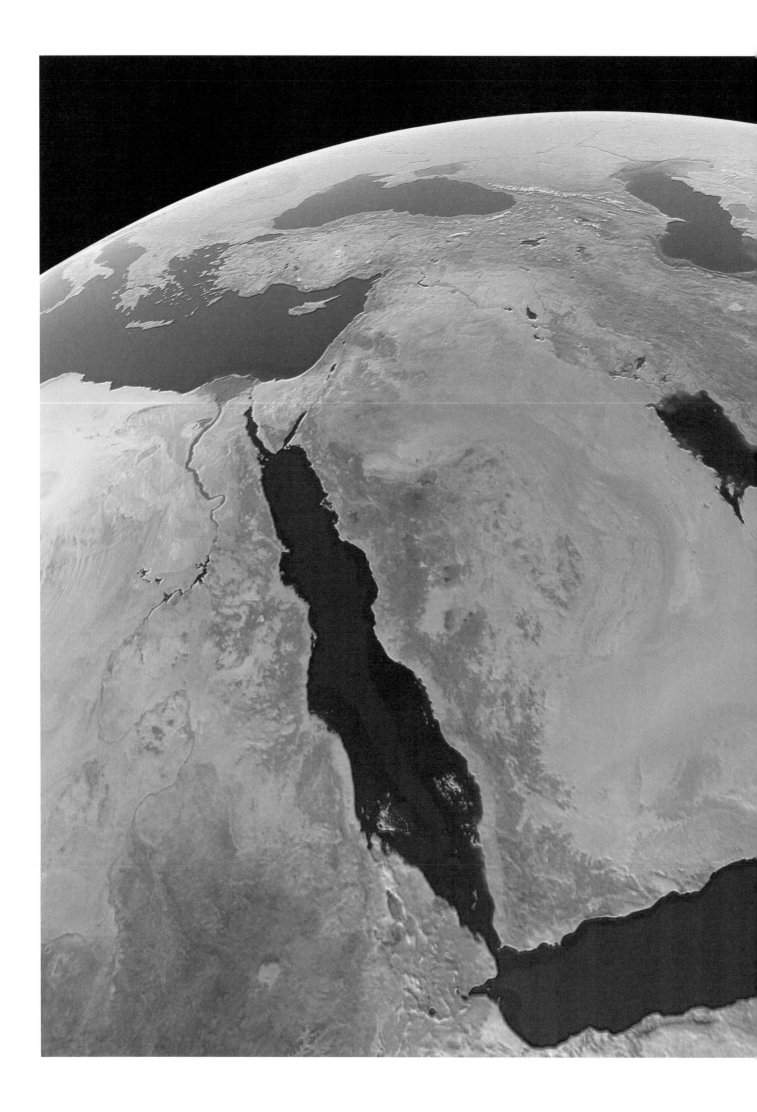

MIDDLE EAST

The Middle East is a region of Asia that is bordered by Asia to the east, Europe to the northwest, Africa to the southwest, and the Mediterranean Sea to the west.

Middle East Overview

Many of today's countries of the Middle
East were formed from the partitioning
of the Ottoman Empire.

Turkey Political

Turkey straddles eastern
Europe and western
Asia. It is divided into
81 provinces, which
are further divided into
districts.

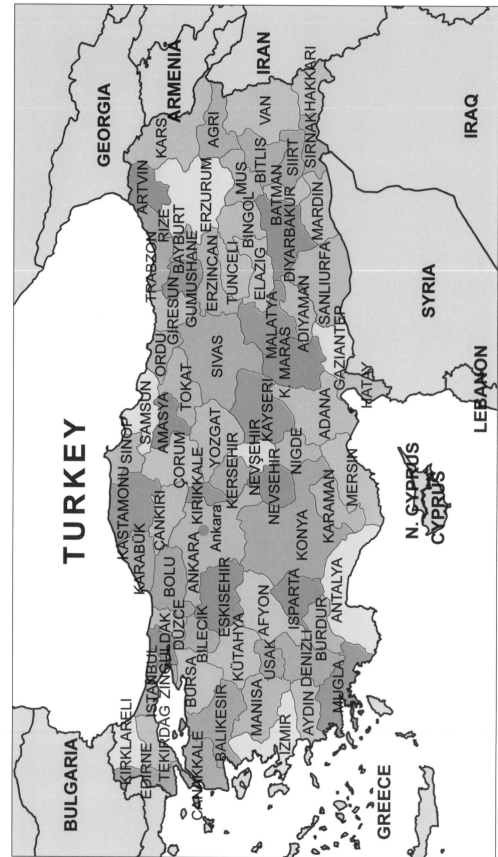

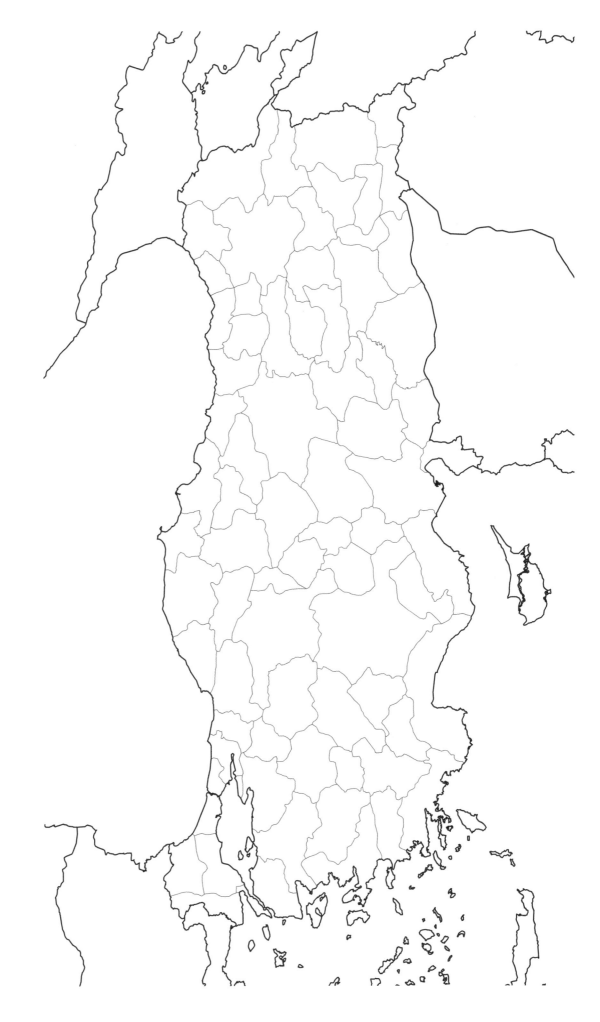

Turkey Topographical

Turkey borders eight countries and covers an area of 302,535 sq mi (783,562 sq km).

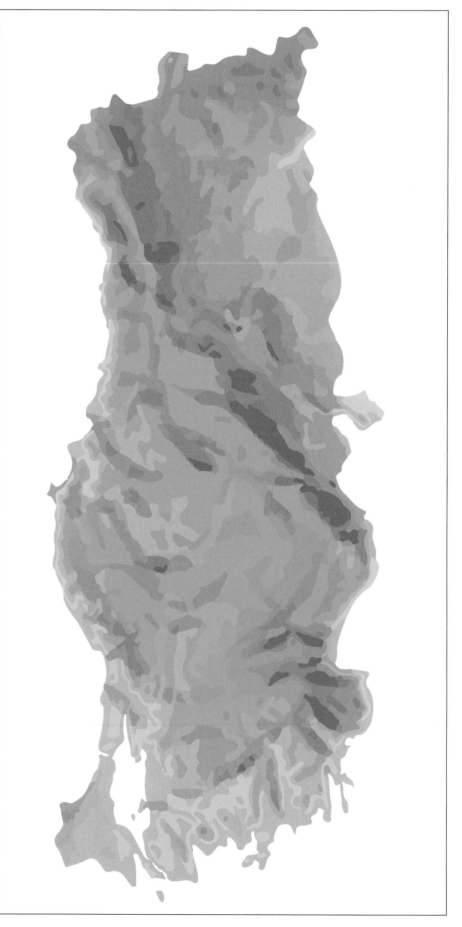

Syria Political

Syria is bordered by Turkey, Lebanon, Israel, Iraq and Jordan. The country is divided into governorates.

Syria Topographical

A home to fertile plains, high mountains and deserts, Syria covers an area of 71,498 sq mi (185,180 sq km).

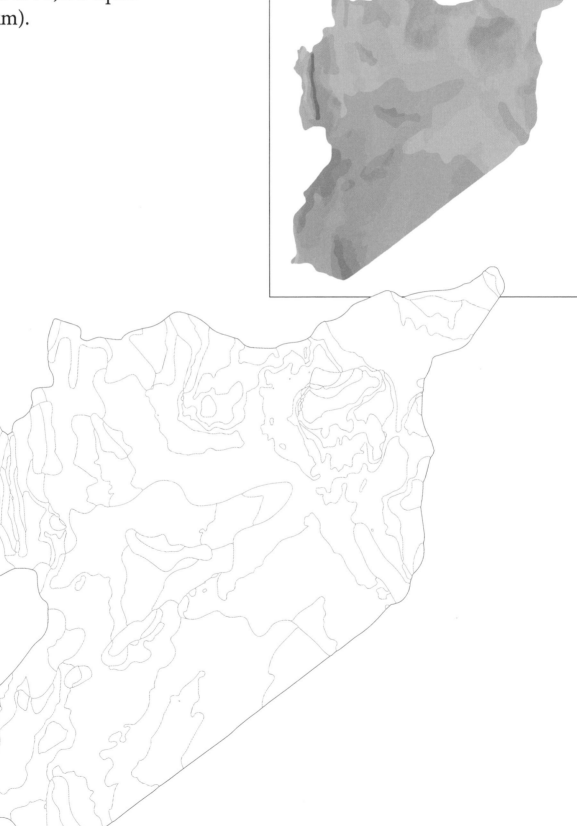

Israel, Lebanon & Jordan Political

Israel is bordered by Lebanon to the north, Syria and Jordan to the east, and Egypt to the south.

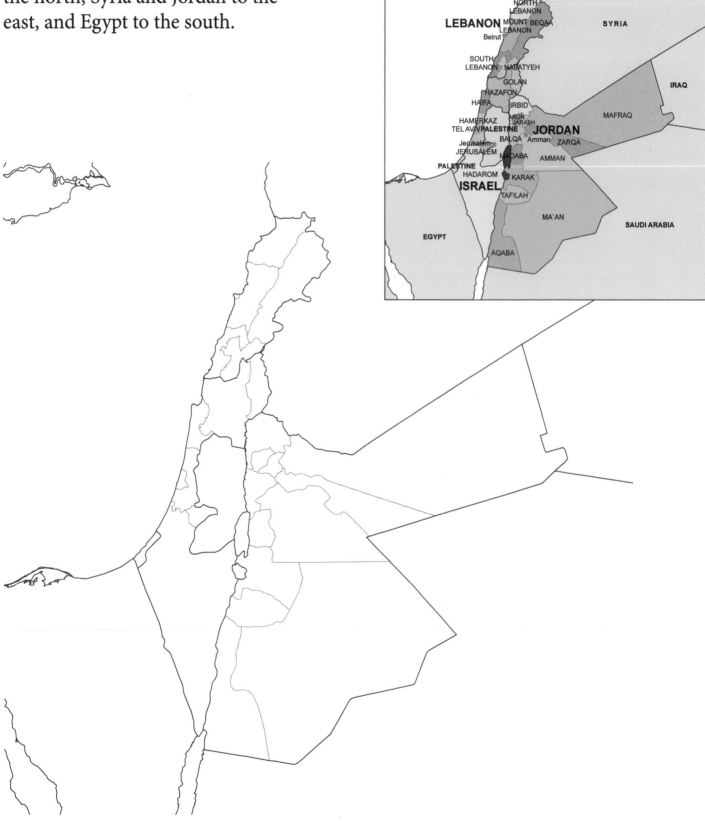

Israel, Lebanon & Jordan Topographical

As a result of its arid climate, the Middle East is home to several of the world's largest deserts.

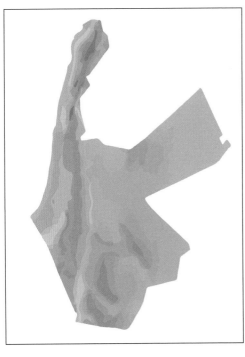

Iraq & Kuwait Topographical

Kuwait is largely a desert, while
Iraq consists of deserts, alluvial
plains and highlands.

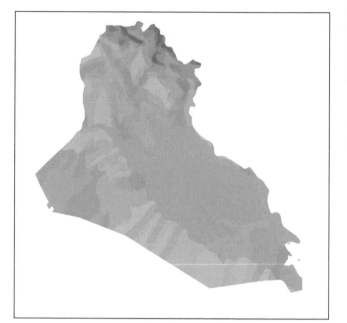

Saudi Arabia, Yemen, Oman & Gulf States Topographical

These countries are all located on the Arabian Peninsula, which is the largest peninsula in the world.

Iran Political

Iran is the only country with
both a Caspian Sea and an Indian
Ocean coastline. It is divided into
31 provinces.

Iran Topographical

Iran, known as Persia until
1935, covers 636,372 sq mi
(1,648,195 sq km).

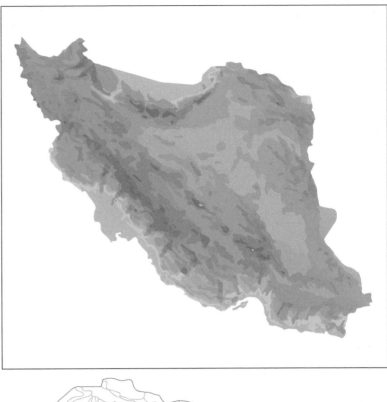

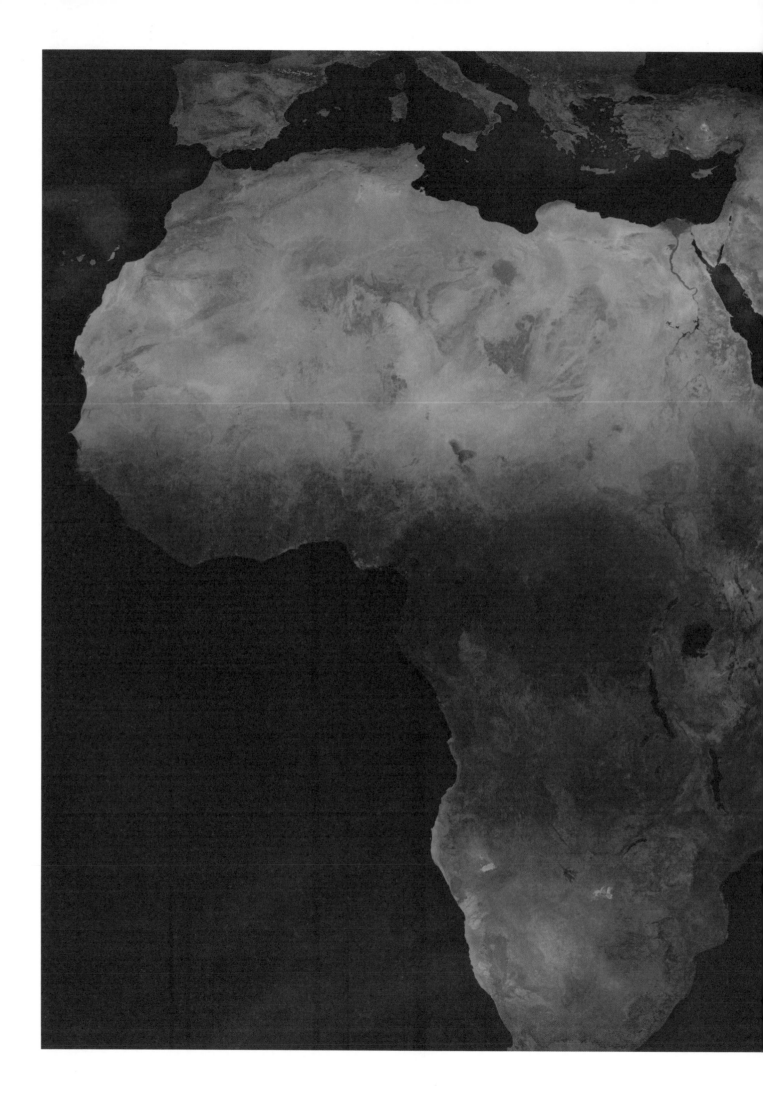

AFRICA

Africa is the second-largest continent in the world, covering an area of 11,724,000 sq mi (30,365,000 sq km), or approximately 6% of the Earth's total surface area.

Africa Overview

Africa is located south of the
Mediterranean Sea and Europe,
with the Indian Ocean to the
southeast and the Atlantic Ocean
to the west.

Egypt Topographical

Egypt links northeast Africa with
the Middle East. It covers an area
of 386,662 sq mi (1,001,450 sq km).

Algeria Topographical

Algeria is the largest country in
Africa, covering an area of 919,595
sq mi (2,381,741 sq km).

DRC Congo Topographical

Covering an area of 905,355 sq mi (2,344,858 sq km), the Democratic Republic of Congo is the largest country in Africa.

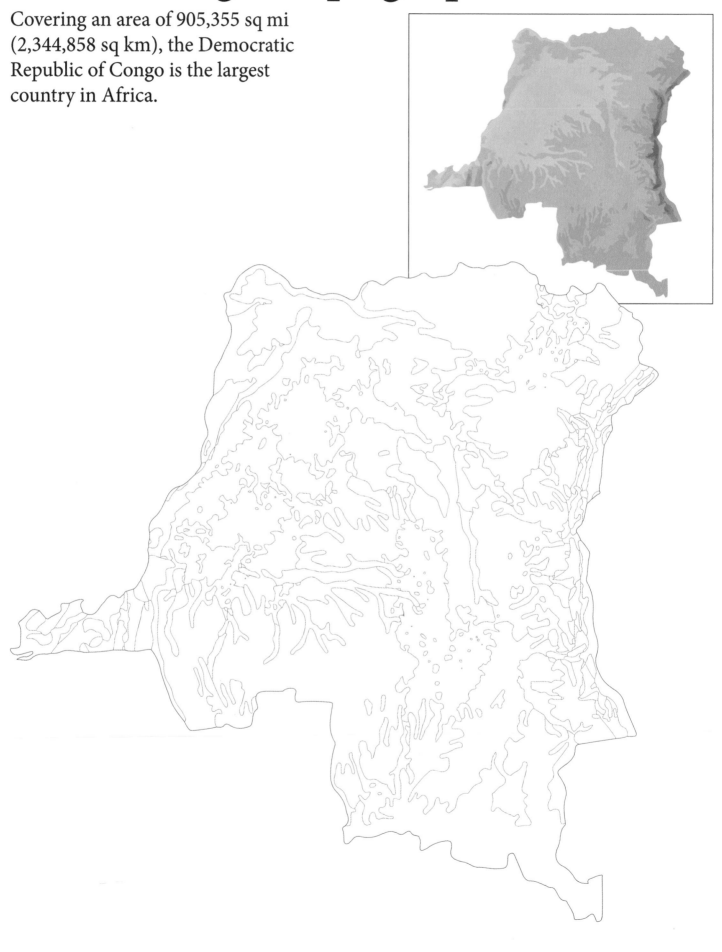

Tanzania Topographical

Tanzania covers an area of 365,755
sq mi (947,300 sq km) and is
known for its vast wilderness areas.

Kenya Topographical

Kenya is located on the
Equator in East Africa and
covers an area of 224,081 sq mi
(580,367 sq km).

Sudan Topographical

Sudan is the third-largest
country in Africa, covering
an area of 718,723 sq mi
(1,861,484 sq km).

Nigeria Topographical

Nigeria is often referred to as the 'Giant of Africa', owing to its large population and economy. It covers an area of 356,669 sq mi (923,768 sq km).

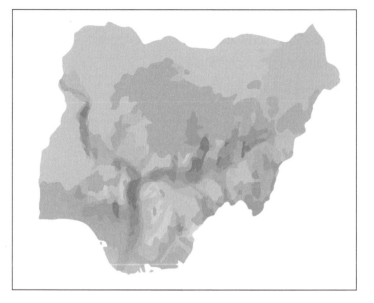

Niger Topographical

Named after the Niger River, Niger
covers an area of 490,349 sq mi
(1,270,000 sq km).

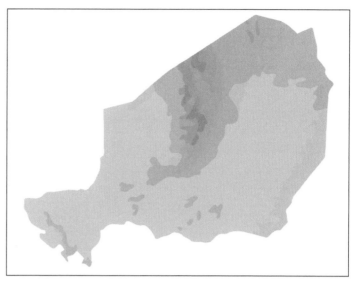

Ethiopia Topographical

A landlocked country in the Horn
of Africa, Ethiopia covers an area
of 426,373 sq mi (1,104,300 sq km).

The Nile

The longest river in Africa, the Nile
measures 4,258 mi (6,853 km).

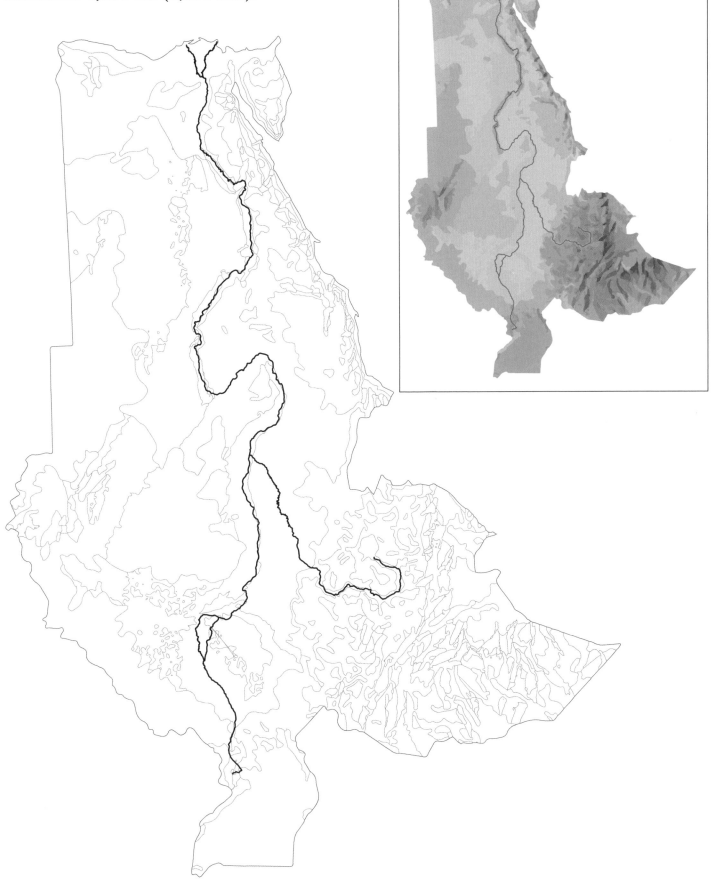

North Africa Political

The northernmost region of North Africa comprises Western Sahara, Morocco, Algeria, Tunisia, Libya, Egypt and Sudan.

North Africa Topographical

The Sahara Desert covers most of North Africa. It is the third-largest desert in the world and covers 3.6 million sq mi (9.2 million sq km).

West Africa Political

West Africa covers about one-fifth of Africa and is divided into 15 countries.

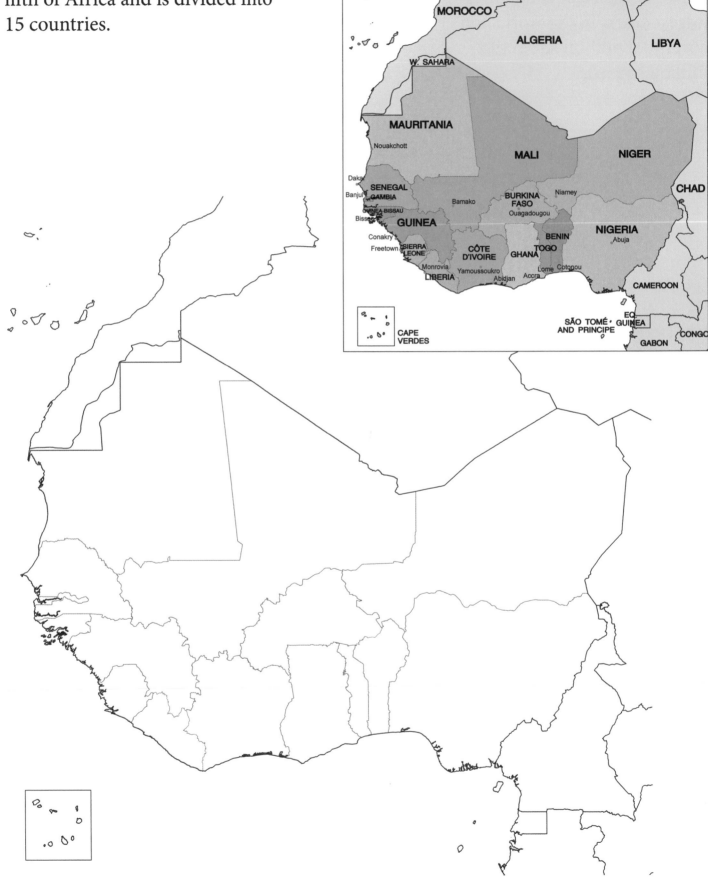

West Africa Topographical

West Africa stretches from the dry
Sahara Desert in the north to lush
rainforests in the south.

Central Africa Political

Central Africa is the heart of the African subcontinent. The largest countries in this region are Democratic Republic of Congo, Sudan, Chad and Angola.

Central Africa Topographical

Central Africa straddles the
Equator and is drained largely by
the Congo River system.

South Africa Political

South Africa is divided into nine provinces, the largest of which is Northern Cape.

South Africa Topographical

South Africa is a country on the
southernmost tip of the continent
of South Africa. The country
covers an area of 470,693 sq mi
(1,219,090 sq km).

Southern African Countries Political

Southern Africa is home to many
vastly different countries.

Southern African Countries Topographical

The terrain of Southern Africa is varied, ranging from forest and grasslands to deserts. It has both low-lying coastal areas and mountains.

The Horn of Africa Topographical

The peninsula in the northeastern part of Africa is known as the Horn of Africa. It comprises Somalia, Ethiopia, Djibouti and Eritrea.

Madagascar Topographical

Madagascar is the fourth-largest island in the world, covering an area of 226,658 sq mi (587,041 sq km).

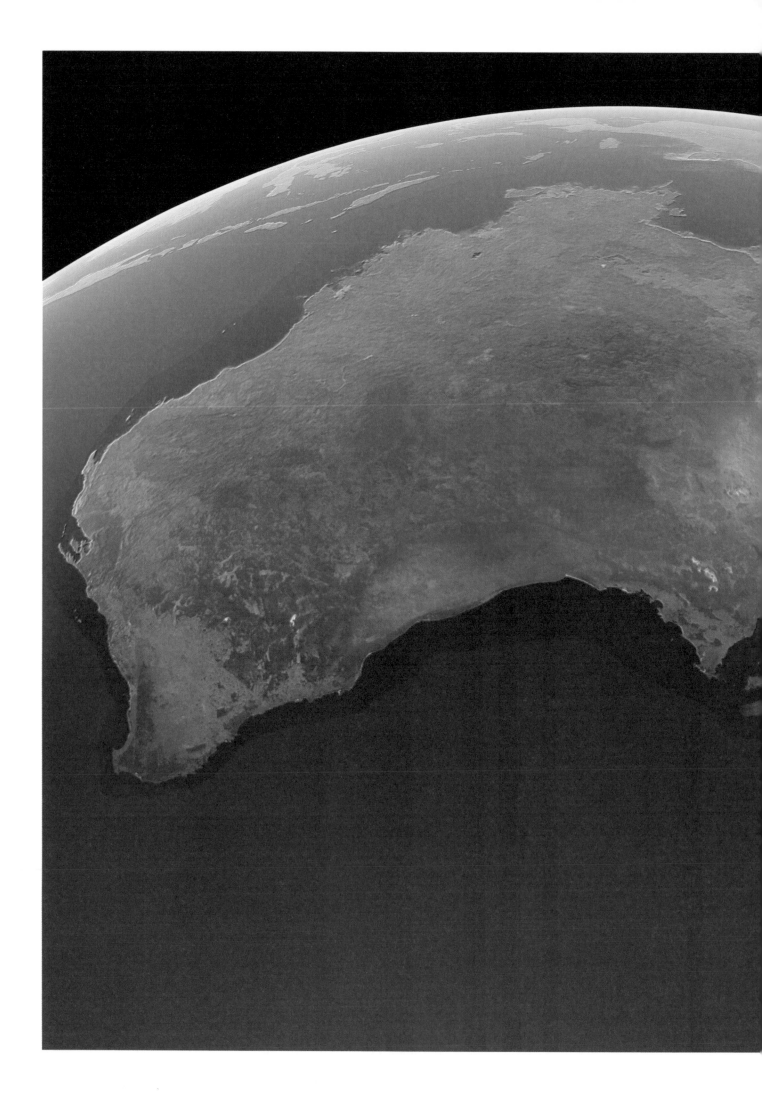

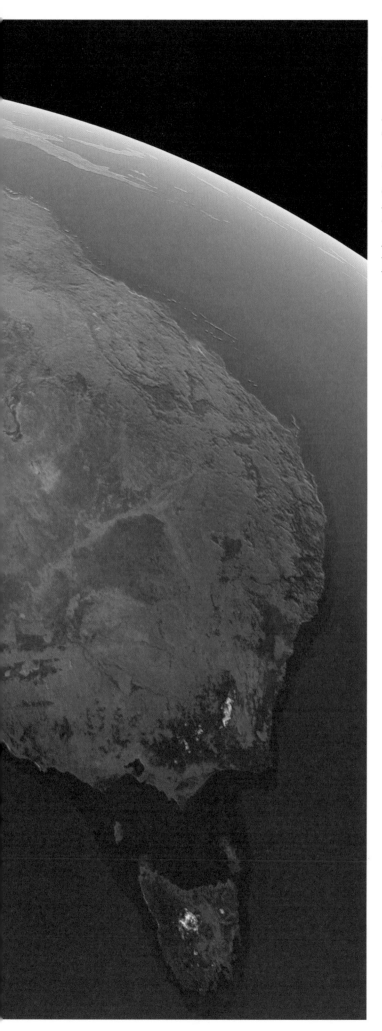

AUSTRALASIA

Australasia is a region within Oceania. The countries, islands and regions that comprise Australasia vary, but the most commonly used include Australia, New Zealand and Papua New Guinea. Australasia lies entirely in the southern hemisphere.

Australia Political

Australia is divided into six states
and two territories.

Australia Topographical

Australia is the sixth-largest
country in the world, covering
an area of 2,988,901 sq mi
(7,741,220 sq km).

New Zealand Political

New Zealand covers an area of
103,799 sq mi (268,838 sq km) and
is divided into 16 regions.

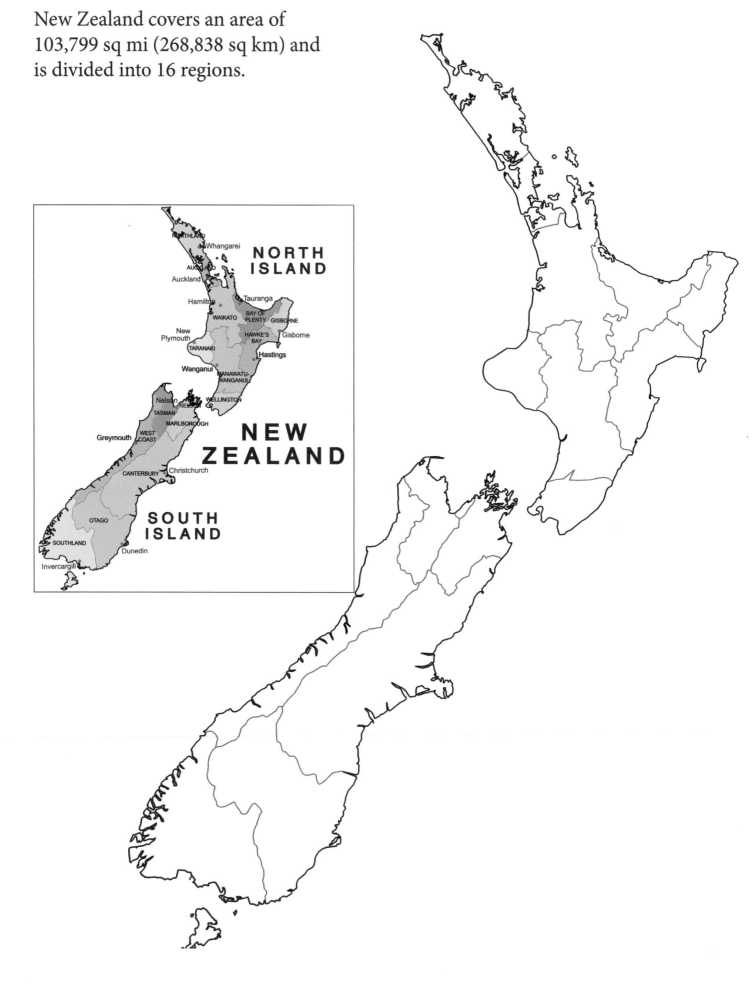

New Zealand Topographical

New Zealand consists of two
main islands – the North Island
and the South Island – and
numerous other small islands.

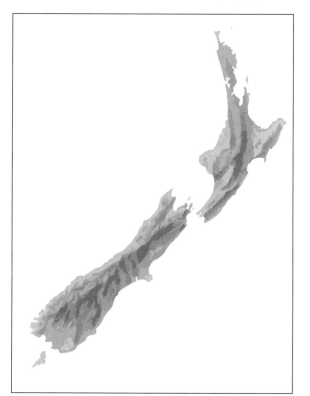

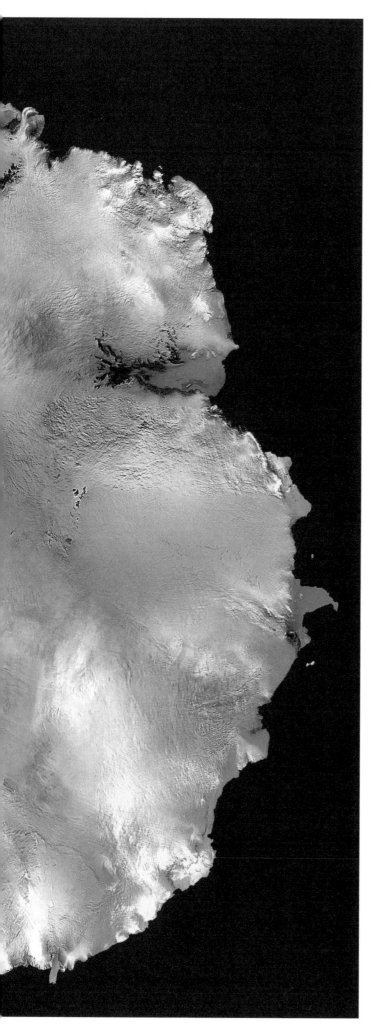

ANTARCTICA

Antarctica is Earth's southernmost
continent, covering an area of 5,405,430
sq mi (14,000,000 sq km).

Antarctica Topographical

Approximately 98% of Antarctica
is covered by ice that averages
1.2 mi (1.9 km) in thickness.